ENCYCLOPEDIA OF THE
Animal World

Vol 2   Aquarium fishes — Biological art

Bay Books Sydney

AQUARIUM FISHES, usually small species, often very colourful, which can be suitably kept in tanks. The aquarium itself is quite as important as the fish that will live in it, both for aesthetic reasons and for the welfare of its inhabitants. The shape of the aquarium greatly affects the amount of oxygen that can diffuse into the water. When filled to the brim, the old-fashioned round goldfish bowl is most unsuitable because of the very small surface area in relation to the depth of the bowl. The best kind of aquarium is one made of angle-iron with glass bottom and sides; its length should be about twice its width and the width about the same as the depth. This will ensure an adequate surface area for the diffusion of oxygen. In deeper tanks and in those which have a high density of fishes, a small air pump should be used. The tank should be covered, both to keep out dust and to prevent certain tropical fishes from jumping out. The cover also provides a screen for whatever lighting is used to illuminate the tank. The type of lighting used is a matter of taste. Some aquarists favour various proprietary brands of strip lighting that simulate daylight, while others insist that ordinary household bulbs, together with daylight, are cheaper and just as good. It is important to remember that light stimulates the growth of algae on the sides of the tank (which can be scraped off with a razor blade or wiped with cotton wool from time to time). Also, a period of darkness is necessary for the well-being of some species of fishes and snails, so that constant lighting is to be avoided. The bottom of the tank should be lined with about 1½ in (4 cm) of coarse sand or gravel which has been sterilized and very thoroughly washed in a bucket under a running tap (the water will cloud if the sand is not clean). The aquarium can be filled either with rain water or with tap water, although the latter should be allowed to stand for a while before the fish are introduced. During the filling of the tank, a sheet of brown paper or plastic spread over the sand will prevent the water clouding. Any decorative stones should be well washed and sterilized before being placed in the tank.

The tank is now ready for plants. Plants from clean but still or sluggish waters can be used but those from fast-flowing streams usually do not survive long in an aquarium. A great range of plants can be bought from dealers, some of them suitable for unheated aquaria but others requiring warm water. The Canadian pond weed *Elodea canadensis* is a cold water species that can adapt well to heated aquaria. The roots should be well anchored in the sand and a small stone can be placed on top of them if there is any tendency for the plant to float upwards. Plants serve three functions in an aquarium. They diffuse oxygen into the water, they provide shelter for the fishes and they add

greatly to the appearance of the aquarium. When stocking with fishes overcrowding should be avoided. A useful rule of thumb is to allow 1 gal (4·5 l) of water for 1 in (2·5 cm) of fish. Above this limit it is advisable to use artificial aeration.

There are three kinds of aquaria: coldwater, tropical and marine. The first is in many ways the simplest, the second the most decorative and the third the greatest challenge to the skill of the aquarist.

Suitable fishes for a coldwater aquarium include the common goldfish *Carassius auratus* (but not the more highly bred varieties), and many of the European and American carp-like fishes found wild in slow-flowing waters. These have the great advantage that they are not carnivorous and will thrive on the easily obtainable commercial fish foods (but not on the standard 'ants eggs'). In Europe, the Golden orfe as well as the tench, rudd and roach are commonly kept in tanks, but once experience is gained many more species can be tried. The North American catfish *Ictalurus* spp. is a most useful addition to the coldwater aquarium because it feeds on the food that has dropped to the bottom and thus keeps the tank clean. Some of the North American sunfishes, such

as the pumpkinseed, are also amenable to aquarium life. Inevitably, however, the aquarist will be drawn to the tropical fishes.

The tropical species are undeniably prettier and more diverse than the coldwater species. For the tropical tank a small heater and thermostat are required to keep the temperature of the water at about 72–78°F (22–25°C). Many more exotic plants can be grown than in the coldwater tank; but unfortunately there will also be a tendency for the glass to become more quickly clouded with algae. The range of fishes available for tropical tanks is now very large and most beginners start with a community tank, that is to say one containing several different but compatible species. The suitability of different species for a community tank has been noted in individual articles in the encyclopedia but as a general rule one is safe with the smaller fishes such as the live-bearing toothcarps (guppies, swordtails, mollies and platys). These fishes will most likely breed in the tank provided that there is enough cover and this adds both to the interest and to the appearance of the tank. Many of the smaller characins (Neon tetras, X-ray fishes, Beacon fishes and Black widows) will make beautiful living patches of colour, particularly the

A well stocked aquarium contains both fish and plants so that natural conditions are reproduced.

worms or finely chopped garden worms. The tropical aquarium is not difficult to maintain provided that it is kept properly heated, clean and not overstocked. Various filtering devices, which are inexpensive and run off the aerating pump, can be used to prevent an accumulation of excess food and faeces on the bottom. The skill, however, is in producing a balanced unit, with the plants supplying oxygen and the fishes keeping the film of algae down to a minimum.

The marine aquarium is the most difficult of all. The problem of obtaining seawater can be resolved by making up the correct solution using sea salt products from a dealer. Nevertheless, it is better if real seawater can be used. The commercial sea fishes are not usually kept as they grow too large, but there are many pretty coral reef fishes that do well in tanks. Compared with freshwater aquaria, seawater aquaria have become popular in relatively recent times and the range of species is still rather small. They are more expensive to keep and dealers usually invest only in species which are easily kept. Malayan angels and Sea horses are always popular and if small live food is available the latter are fairly easy to keep alive. The marine aquarium is not advised for those with limited means.

Fish are very sensitive to certain substances in the water. Copper and zinc are highly toxic and the use of copper or brass pipes for filling the tank should be avoided. Fish are also prone to various diseases, and it is most important to buy fish that appear to be in good condition. A healthy fish swims smoothly and lithely, whereas one that is sickly is dull, listless or erratic, with the fins not erect and their edges often ragged. Avoid buying a fish from an aquarium that contains a sickly fish. Fishes are prone to white spot *Ichthiophthyrius,* fin rot, dropsy and a host of other diseases, for which bathing in solu-

Veil-tailed goldfish.

Catfish *Corydoras elegans*, useful members of the aquarium community as they keep the tank bottom clear of debris

Neon, Glowlight and Cardinal tetras. The smaller barbs are peaceful fishes and fit in well, as also do many of the danios. The cichlids, on the other hand, should be treated with caution since many of them will attack small fishes. Essential to the tropical aquarium are the small catfishes, for example, members of the genus *Corydoras*, since they grub around the bottom and thus keep the tank clean. Another useful addition to the community tank is either a Sucking loach *Gyrinocheilus* spp. or one of the Sucking catfishes (*Otocinclus* or *Plecostomus*). These fishes browse on the algae that grow on the glass or on stones and they again will help to keep the tank clean. Such fishes have the lips expanded to form a disc and when they adhere to the glass it is possible to see their jaws rasping away at the algae.

The larger, and more costly, tropical fishes are best left until experience has been gained with the less expensive ones. Suitable food can be obtained from dealers who sell excellent preparations of dried foods. It is advisable to supplement this occasionally with live food such as *Daphnia,* tubifex

tions of potassium permanganate or salt may provide a cure. The most important thing is to isolate the affected fishes in a separate tank and to diagnose the disease with the aid of one of the many books now available.

There is some evidence that the Egyptians kept fishes not only for eating but also for the pleasure of watching them. The keeping of aquarium fishes has been practised for many centuries in China and the Far East. In Europe and the United States fish keeping has become increasingly popular since the last war and as a result the number of species available has increased enormously. With just a little care and common sense a well-balanced community of fishes can bring colour, interest and beauty into the home.

ARACARIS, small to medium-sized toucans of the forests of Central and South America, belonging to two genera, *Andigena* and *Pteroglossus*. The plumage is usually mainly black dorsally. It can, however, be red, yellow, and black. The long bill has some tooth-like serrations. The diet is fruit, with some insects. Aracaris are highly sociable and usually found in small flocks. They roost communally in cavities in trees, single groups apparently using a number of alternative roosts. The nest is an unlined hole in a tree and two to four rounded white eggs are laid. The young develop very slowly, taking about one and a half months to fledge. They may be fed by a group of adults. FAMILY: Ramphastidae, ORDER: Piciformes, CLASS: Aves.

ARACHNIDS, a class of arthropods, for the most part terrestrial in habit, which include scorpions, spiders, harvestmen, mites and ticks together with some lesser-known groups. During the course of arthropod evolution, two main lines have progressively diverged, one being the so-called 'mandibulate' line which gave rise to the crustaceans, myriapods and insects, the other being the 'chelicerate' line which produced the arachnids. Although it is not known at what point the common arthropod ancestral stock divided to allow the development of these two great lineages, the fossil record tells us that the arachnids are probably the oldest terrestrial arthropods, and fossil scorpions very similar in appearance to those alive today have been found in rock formations over 300 million years old.

Insects and arachnids. These are the two most successful groups of land-dwelling arthropods and, at first sight, it seems strange that the two should have been able to evolve, side by side and often competing with each other, with such obvious success. In addition to the direct, and legendary, conflict between the spider and the fly, both groups

The curiously shaped spider *Gasteracanthus* sp, of East Africa.

include many predators, parasites and plant-feeding species which ravage not only man, his domestic animals and crops, but also a wide range of wild animals and plants. This convergence of habits can bring insects and arachnids into direct competition, and it might be expected that one of these two groups would have become overwhelmingly dominant. It is true that the insects, of which there are more than 700,000 species, have diversified to a greater extent than the arachnids with less than 100,000 species, but the latter are by no means insignificant and, indeed, have become more successful than the insects in some situations.

The key to the continued success of the arachnids lies in their ability to colonize habitats in which insects, for one reason or another, have not been able to achieve a supremacy. Both groups include a number of species which have become adapted to an aquatic mode of life, but the arachnids have been more successful in colonizing marine situations, while the insects have undoubtedly done better in freshwater. Parasitic forms occur in both groups, but the arachnids have been most successful in producing blood-sucking external parasites, whereas many of the parasitic insects have adapted more efficiently to invading the internal tissues of their hosts. On land, the insects have made good use of their wings as adults to become airborne, their great mobility allowing wide dispersal and a way of escaping the attentions of earthbound predators, many of which are arachnids. The latter have never discovered the secret of aerial flight and are destined to remain close to the ground. Consequently, while insects hold sway in the air, the arachnids have flourished in many of the habitats provided by low vegetation, leaf litter and the soil and in many ways they are more successful than the insects in these situations. Eloquent testimony to this is given by the many millions of arachnids that occur to the acre in soils under grassland and woodland. Very often these arachnids are minute in size, but theirs is a vital role in controlling populations of insect pests and in the various biological processes that promote the fertility of the soil.

Classification. The 60,000 or so species can be classified into a number of orders, the exact number varying with the person doing the classifying. As a conservative estimate, ten such groupings can be recognized and at least 90% of all arachnids can be included in two of these, namely the Araneida, or spiders, and the Acari, or the mites and ticks. Both of these groups are widely distributed throughout the world, the mites even more so than the spiders, for they have become established on the Antarctic continent in habitats where few other terrestrial animals are able to survive. Both groups are abundant in low vegetation and in the upper organic layers of the soil in temperate and tropical regions. Tropical spiders include the large and fearsome mygalomorphs, the 'Bird-eating' or Tarantula spiders, which have a reputation for their poisonous bite although few, if any, are dangerous to man.

Many spiders habitually occur in or near human habitations. In Britain the common orb-weaving Garden spider *Araneus diadematus* is easily recognizable by its relatively large size and distinctive colour-pattern; *Tegenaria domestica* is the common European House spider, while members of the family Theridiidae, which includes the poisonous American Black widow, are the familiar cobweb or comb-footed spiders. Although spiders are mainly confined to terrestrial situations, one species which occurs in Europe and Asia, *Argyroneta aquatica,* can swim under water and constructs a bell-shaped web in this medium. It is not truly aquatic, however, for it traps a film of air around its body by means of long hairs and fills its bell-shaped nest with air. However, it is the habitats on or near the soil that are richly colonized by spiders and in the northern hemisphere one of the commonest and most abundant families found in these localities is the Linyphiidae, the 'hammock-web' or 'sheet-web' spiders.

The Acari, or mites, is a group of arachnids about which relatively little is known, although the rate at which new species are being discovered suggests that this group is by far the largest of the arachnids. These are minute animals, easily overlooked on account of their small size, abounding in the

Scorpion from the Isle of Elba *Euscorpius flavicaudis*.

Ticks on the skin of a hedgehog.

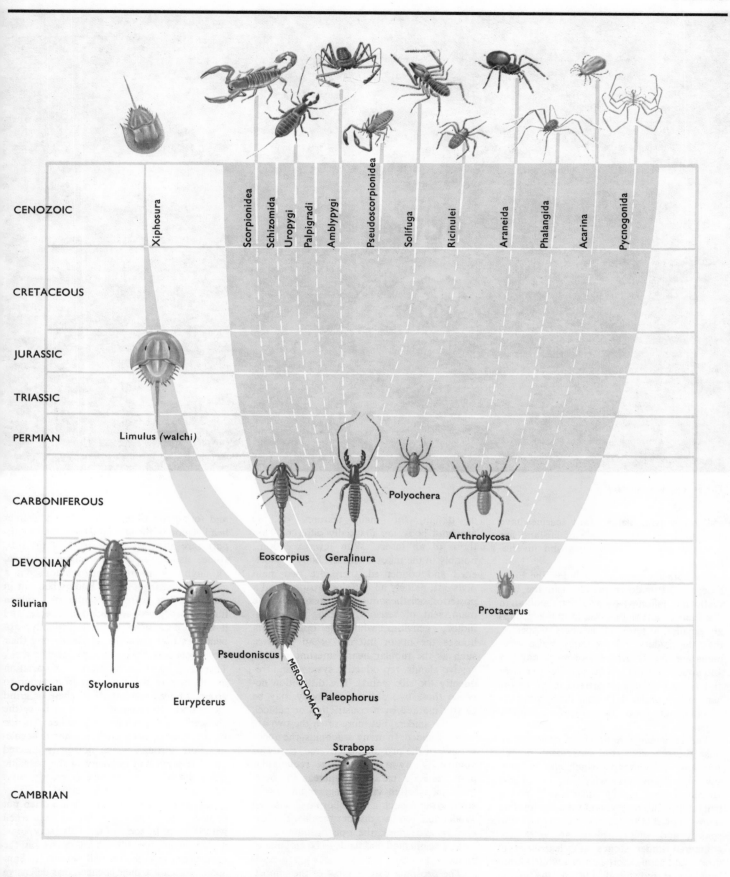

CENOZOIC

CRETACEOUS

JURASSIC

TRIASSIC

PERMIAN

CARBONIFEROUS

DEVONIAN

Silurian

Ordovician

CAMBRIAN

Xiphosura

Scorpionidea

Schizomida

Uropygi

Palpigradi

Amblypygi

Pseudoscorpionidea

Solifuga

Ricinulei

Araneida

Phalangida

Acarina

Pycnogonida

Limulus (walchi)

Eoscorpius

Geralinura

Polyochera

Arthrolycosa

Protacarus

Stylonurus

Eurypterus

Pseudoniscus

MEROSTOMACA

Paleophorus

Strabops

Evolutionary history of the Arachnida, as indicated by the fossil record, from the ancestral *Strabops* to the present-day. To the left, the Eurypterids died out early, and to the right of these is the line of Horseshoe crabs, all extinct except for the few species living today. The main stem gave rise to the modern scorpions, whipscorpions, booklice, spiders, harvestmen and ticks, with (extreme right at top) the pycnogonids or Sea spiders.

The St. Eustatius spider.

soil and on living plants. Many acarines have developed a parasitic mode of life and are common both on vertebrates and invertebrates.

Two other groups of arachnids, the False scorpions (Pseudoscorpiones) and the harvestmen (Opiliones) are also cosmopolitan in distribution although both of these groups are smaller, in terms of numbers of species, than the spiders and the mites. False scorpions are mainly denizens of moist habitats and flourish best in leaf litter, under tree bark and in rock crevices, whereas many of the harvestmen prefer the rather drier, more exposed, conditions of the soil surface and low vegetation.

The remaining six arachnid orders comprise the scorpions, the sunspiders, ricinuleids and three groups which can be considered collectively as whipscorpions. These arachnids are mainly distributed in the tropics and subtropics, and together total no more than 2,000 species. Scorpions, sunspiders and whipscorpions are often encountered under stones and leaf litter in desert and semi-desert regions, while ricinuleids prefer moist leaf litter or the humid environment of caves.

Structure. Although basically arthropod in design, the main features of the arachnid body are markedly different from those of an insect. With few exceptions, notably in the mites where the body is shortened and condensed, there are two main divisions, namely an anterior prosoma and a posterior opisthosoma. The prosoma is the main seat of sensory, feeding and locomotory activities, while the opisthosoma houses the major internal organ systems, such as the tubular heart, intestine and digestive glands, reproductive system, and frequently the silk glands. The distinction between these two parts of the body may be clearly marked by a constriction or pedicel, as in the spiders, but more often the two are broadly joined. In many arachnids, the upper surface of the prosoma is covered, partly or completely, by a single, large rectangular plate, called a carapace, whereas the opisthosoma is often visibly segmented and in some groups, such as the scorpions, may be subdivided into two distinct regions. In most spiders and mites, the opisthosoma is not clearly segmented and tends to be globular in shape.

The prosoma carries most of the important appendages; typically these consist of six pairs, comprising two pairs of mouthparts and four pairs of legs. There is no distinct head region in the arachnids and the mouthparts are attached to the front of the prosoma, usually in a conspicuous position, although in some mites they are housed in a cavity at the front of the body when not in use. The first pair of mouthparts, which function as 'jaws', are called chelicerae, and it is the possession of these distinctive appendages that gives the arachnids and their close relatives the name of 'chelicerates'. There is a considerable amount of variation in the form of the chelicerae from group to group. Many arachnids tear, chew or grind their food before eating it and in these the chelicerae are developed as toothed pincers. In the spiders, each chelicera has a needle-like fang through which poison is injected into the prey, and in many of the parasitic mites the whole appendage is greatly elongate and is used as a piercing stylet.

The chelicerae of arachnids are often put to uses other than those directly concerned with feeding. In some of the False scorpions, a duct from the silk gland opens on the chelicerae through a small spinneret. Sunspiders often use their chelicerae as defensive weapons, while male ticks use their chelicerae to transfer packets of sperm from their own genital aperture to the reproductive tract of the female.

The second pair of mouthparts, called pedipalps because they often resemble walking legs in general appearance, are clothed with sensory hairs and often function as feelers, tasting food or exploring the environment. Sunspiders use their palps as accessory walking legs, while in the scorpions, False scorpions and certain of the whipscorpions they are formidable weapons, fashioned as prehensile claws, for defence and food capture. False scorpions inject poison into their prey through the tip of the pincer-like palp, while in male spiders part of the palp is enlarged to form a reservoir in which sperm is stored prior to being transferred to the genital tract of the female.

With the exception of the larval stages of mites and ricinuleids which usually have three pairs of legs, the immature and adult stages of the arachnids are equipped with four pairs of legs. These are well furnished with sensory hairs and, in addition to their locomotory function, the first pair is also used as feelers in some of the spiders, harvestmen and mites. The remaining legs may also serve for digging soil burrows (scorpions), food capture (harvestmen), combing out silk (spiders), as claspers during copulation (mites and ticks) or to hold the egg mass (ricinuleids and some Water mites).

Silk. On the underside of the opisthosoma are the genital and anal openings, the former usually being situated far forwards, the latter terminal or sub-terminal. At the tip of the abdomen of most spiders are the spinnerets, small conical or cylindrical tubes, varying in number from one to four pairs. It is through these spigots that silk, manufactured in glands situated deep in the body,

is pulled out as fine threads. Silk is a valuable commodity to the spider, and the various uses to which it can be put have no doubt contributed in no small measure to the great success of this group of arachnids. By creating silken snares and webs, spiders have been enabled to prey on flying insects, despite the fact that they themselves cannot fly. They wrap their eggs in silken cocoons to protect the young when they are at their most vulnerable. Nests, retreats and burrows are often lined with silk, and even among hunting spiders, which do not spin webs, silken drag lines are trailed to prevent the spider from being blown away or otherwise dislodged. These drag lines also serve to lead the males of certain Wolf spiders to the females and, indeed, silk often plays an important part in the mating and courtship ritual. Many male spiders spin a small silken mat on which they deposit sperm prior to filling the sperm reservoirs of the palps. A sexual encounter with a female is full of potential danger for the male, since she often tends to be cannibalistic. Before he can approach with any confidence, it is sometimes necessary to bind his partner lightly in a silken cocoon. Silk also has a locomotory function, for although spiders cannot fly, they can float in air currents. This is particularly true of young spiders, and may be an important factor in their dispersal. Such aerial transport is achieved by using silken strands, gossamer threads, which keep the spider buoyant and allow it to be carried in wind currents, sometimes to heights of several thousand feet.

Generally speaking, most of the important parts of the sensory equipment of an arachnid, such as hairs and eyes, are carried on the front part of the body, the mouthparts and the legs. One important exception is a

pair of sensory combs, or pectines, found only in the scorpions and attached on the underside of the abdomen just behind the genital aperture. These combs can be orientated so that the tips of the teeth touch the surface of the ground, and they may be used to detect mechanical vibrations or to provide information about the nature of the substratum.

The arachnid eye is a simple structure and, in many cases, unlike the compound eye of the insect, is probably incapable of forming a distinct image. For many arachnids, sight must rank second in importance to the sense of touch and in some of the nocturnal and soil-dwelling groups, such as certain harvestmen and many mites, eyes are reduced in number or absent. When present, the eyes often occur in groups on the sides or the front of the carapace covering the prosoma. Vision in some of the hunting spiders, notably the Wolf spiders, Jumping spiders and Crab spiders, is well developed and the Wolf spiders, at least, can orientate themselves with respect to the position of the sun or the pattern of polarized light in the sky, in much the same way as can certain insects.

Habitat. Apart from the Aquatic spider *Argyroneta* and the Water mites, the arachnid story is one of adaptation to life on land and success is often measured by the extent to which water can be conserved and the desiccating power of the atmosphere resisted. This means, more than anything else perhaps, that ways have to be developed to curtail water loss without impairing the efficiency of the respiratory system. Insects have achieved this by possessing a waterproofed body covering and a tracheal system of respiration which allows the water loss to be controlled through spiracles which can be closed, when necessary, by valves. To a large extent, the arachnids parallel the insects in this respect, for their body covering is essentially similar to that of the insects and the respiratory system of the majority of arachnids is of the tracheal type. However, there are variations in the character of this system and these are frequently related to the mode of life of the species concerned. A primitive type of respiratory structure, called the lung book, is found in scorpions, whipscorpions and some of the spiders. The lung book is a legacy from some early aquatic ancestor which probably respired through a series of plate-like gills grouped one on top of the other like the leaves of a book. Such structures occur on the underside of the abdomen in Horseshoe crabs. In order for this system to function efficiently on land without involving unrestricted water loss, the leaf-like gills are withdrawn into pouches, made by invaginations of the body cuticle, and the cavity so formed connects with the exterior by a small pore. This pouch, containing a cluster of respiratory leaflets, is the 'lung

A non-web spinning spider, *Dysdera crocata*, of Europe.

book', and there are four pairs of these in the scorpions, two pairs in the whipscorpions and the mygalomorph 'tarantulas' and a single pair in many other groups of spiders. A second type of respiratory system, the tracheal system is also present. In the False scorpions, harvestmen, ricinuleids, sunspiders and many of the mites, the lung books have disappeared and only the tracheal system remains, while in some of the small soil-dwelling mites there are neither lung books nor tracheae, the animals respiring across the body surface which, as a prerequisite, is not waterproofed. In such cases the animals must remain almost constantly in the very humid conditions provided by a subterranean environment.

Feeding. Arachnids are mostly carnivorous in habit, preying on other arthropods. Some are active hunters, stalking and capturing prey with the aid of their prehensile mouthparts, others construct snares in the form of silken webs in which the prey becomes entangled and can be easily narcotized by an injection of poison. Some of the predatory mites use larger beetles and flies as a means of transport from one feeding ground to another, attaching to the host and thus being carried around. This habit, which is also shown by some False scorpions, is called *phoresy, and it may represent an intermediate stage in the evolution of external parasitism. Ectoparasitism among the arachnids is restricted to certain groups of Acari, particularly but not exclusively to the ticks, which are often serious pests of man and his domestic animals, not only because of their blood-sucking habit, but also because these parasites serve as agents for the transmission of diseases, such as Scrub typhus, Relapsing fever and Red-water fever. Very few arachnids occur as internal parasites of other animals; this habit is restricted to a few groups of mites which infest the nasal cavities, tracheae or lungs of reptiles, birds and mammals, or the tracheal system of such insects as the honeybee. Notable departures from the carnivorous feeding habit occur in only one of the major groups of arachnids, the Acari, in which the habit of feeding on plant material has undoubtedly developed independently in a relatively large number of families. Indeed, one whole order of mites, the *Moss mites or Cryptostigmata, consists almost exclusively of plant-feeding forms. Among these mites, those that consume living plant material can be distinguished from the detritus-feeding species which take only decomposing plant material. To the former group belong many important agricultural pests, such as the Spider mites and the Gall mites which damage or destroy cultivated crops either as a direct consequence of their feeding on the plant tissue, or because they act as agents for the transmission of plant viruses. The detri-

tus-feeders have a much less dramatic impact on the human economy, but nevertheless play a vital role in the decomposition processes that occur in the soil on which living plants rely for their source of nutrients.

Breeding. Many of the carnivorous arachnids are extremely aggressive, not only to other groups of animals but also to their own kin. They can rarely, if ever, live in harmony with each other and this raises a serious problem as far as reproduction is concerned, since only a few groups of mites, scorpions and spiders can produce viable eggs without cross-fertilization. Thus, the male arachnid usually has to 'persuade' the female to curb her aggressive instincts towards him if the eggs are to be fertilized. Few male arachnids, notably the harvestmen and certain groups of mites, possess a penis and, as a result, direct copulation is the exception rather than the rule. In some of the mites, fertilization occurs without the males and females even meeting. The male deposits a spermatophore, a globular packet of sperm carried on a stalk, by sticking it in the ground and as the female passes over this spermatophore she manoeuvres the sperm packet into her genital tract. The same method of sperm transfer occurs in the scorpions, whipscorpions and False scorpions, but in these cases the male actually guides the female until she is in a position to pick up the sperm. The necessary

physical contact which must occur between the two partners during this procedure is often built into an elaborate courtship ritual designed to pacify the female and to inhibit her from attacking and devouring the male. Details of this behaviour pattern vary from group to group, although as a general rule the courting male quietens his partner by stroking and caressing her with his mouthparts and front legs. A similar courtship pattern is shown by the spiders, sunspiders, ticks and ricinuleids in which a greater degree of intimacy is achieved and the male actually inserts the sperm mass into the genital aperture of the female, using his mouthparts or, occasionally, his legs. In some of the hunting spiders, visual stimuli play an important part in the courtship ritual, with the male displaying brightly coloured parts of the body and legs. Visual display is unimportant in most of the other arachnids.

Parental behaviour. Many arachnids show some form of care towards their young, at least for a short period of time immediately after birth. Spiders and False scorpions deposit their eggs in a protective silk cocoon which may be attached to the substratum. The adult Wolf spider carries the egg sac which is held on the spinnerets and by alternately exposing the eggs to the warmth of the sun or shading them if the temperature rises too high, it ensures that the

Table showing the main groups of present day Arachnida. From a hypothetical ancestor have arisen the scorpions (left), the many kinds of spiders (top two rows), the false scorpions, harvestman and mites (bottom row to right).

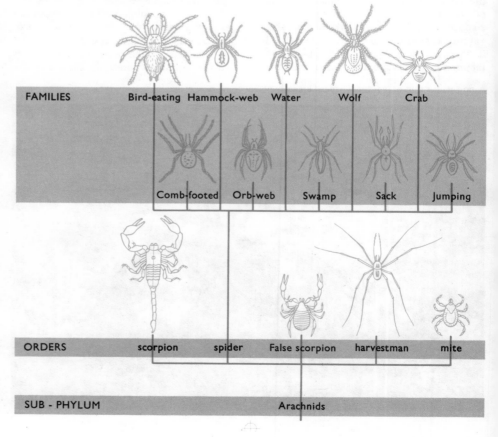

FAMILIES	Bird-eating	Hammock-web	Water	Wolf	Crab
	Comb-footed	Orb-web	Swamp	Sack	Jumping

ORDERS	scorpion	spider	False scorpion	harvestman	mite

SUB - PHYLUM			Arachnids		

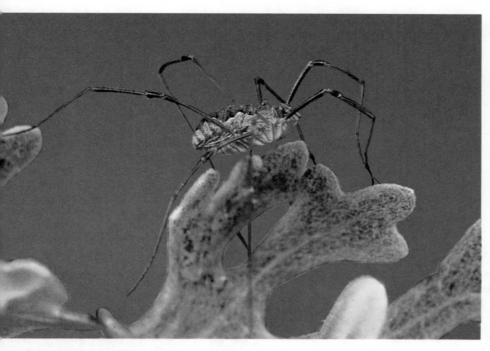

Harvestman, long-legged relative of spiders.

embryos develop under the most suitable conditions. After emerging from the egg sac, young Wolf spiders climb on the mother's back where they remain for a week or more. A similar form of parental care is shown by the whipscorpions, in which the eggs are carried in a sac attached to the underside of the mother's body and in the scorpions which give birth to living young. Parental care is not shown by the harvestmen and it is the exception rather than the rule in the mites. CLASS: Arachnida, PHYLUM: Arthropoda.   J.A.W.

ARAPAIMA *Arapaima gigas,* a large and rather primitive fish of the Amazon basin. The arapaima is the largest member of the family Osteoglossidae or bonytongues and is one of the largest of all freshwater fishes, reaching about 9 ft (2·8 m) in length (reports of fishes reaching 15 ft (4·3 m) are probably exaggerated). It has a long, sinuous body, with the dorsal and anal fins set far back, the scales on the body thick and large, and the mouth not protrusible. The family to which the arapaima belongs is of considerable scientific interest because it appears to have been fairly widespread in Eocene times but is now represented by species isolated in South America, Africa, Australia and parts of the Indo-Australian Archipelago.

There are two species of osteoglossids in South America, the arapaima and the related arawana *Osteoglossum bicirrhosum.* Curiously enough, the most suitable bait for the arapaima seems to be the arawana. The arapaima is an avid fish-eater and even the armoured catfishes are readily taken. The

Arapaima, largest freshwater fish.

front part of the body is a bronze-green, but nearer the tail red patches appear and the tail itself can be mottled orange and green. Arapaima live in murky waters and the swimbladder has been adapted for breathing atmospheric oxygen, the adult fishes coming to the surface about once every 12 minutes to breathe.

Male arapaima guard the eggs, which are laid in holes dug out of the soft bottom of the river bed. An interesting method has been evolved to prevent the newly hatched larvae from straying too far and thus being snapped up by predators. For three months the young fishes stay with the father and during that time they remain close to his head. What keeps them there is a substance secreted by the male from glands opening from the back of the head. This was formerly thought to be a kind of 'milk' on which the young fed but it is now known to be merely a substance that attracts the young. Should the male be killed while looking after the young, the latter will disperse until they encounter another male and will join his brood. The males apparently do not eat the young of their own species.

The arapaima has a rapid growth and a 6 in (15 cm) specimen at the London Zoo grew to nearly 6 ft (1·8 m) in a period of six years. FAMILY: Osteoglossidae, ORDER: Osteoglossiformes, CLASS: Pisces.

ARAPAIMA, the arapaima is of interest because its red blood corpuscles are like those of man and its blood clots on exposure to the air, and also because of the way the parents guard the young. The young swim near the surface above the head of the male who rises repeatedly to gulp air. The colour of their bodies matches that of the male's head which turns black in the breeding season. The female circles the male and the crowd of young, fending off predators.

ARCHAEOCYATHA, a group of marine animals which lived in Lower Cambrian times. They show some resemblance to sponges but are now considered to be a distinct phylum. Their skeletons were made

of calcium carbonate but lack the spicules so characteristic of sponges. Each had the form of a small cone attached to the substratum at its pointed end, the walls of which were generally double with the two layers connected by a variety of plates and struts and perforated by numerous pores. It is thought that soft tissues enclosed the skeletal wall leaving an open cavity in the centre of the cone. The animals were probably filter-feeders drawing a current of water through the walls and expelling it vertically from a central opening. The Archaeocyatha are the earliest known reef-forming animals. CLASS: Archaeocyatha, PHYLUM: Porifera.

ARCHAEOPTERYX *Archaeopteryx lithographica,* the oldest known bird. Three specimens have been found in the Jurassic limestone of Bavaria laid down some 150 million years ago. The specimens were found with other fossil materials in 1861, 1877 and 1956 in quarries of lithographic stone, all within 9 miles (15 km) of each other. Two separate feather fossils have also been found. One, found in another quarry in the same area in 1860, is almost certainly from *Archaeopteryx,* but the other, from a Jurassic lithographic limestone quarry in Spain, is of uncertain origin.

The *Archaeopteryx* fossils are so well preserved that much of the structure is clear, demonstrating that although the animal possessed many reptilian features it also had a number of avian characteristics, including feathers, meriting inclusion in the class Aves.

The reptilian characters of *Archaeopteryx* are as follows. There are 20 elongated caudal vertebrae supporting a tail as long as the body, as in most reptiles but in no known birds. The sacral vertebrae are only six in number, there being no synsacrum of fused vertebrae as in birds. The articular surfaces of the vertebrae are simply concave discs, not saddle shaped as in birds. The ribs are simple and unjointed and about 12 dermal abdominal ribs, or gastralia, are present. The metacarpal bones are not fused together, as in a bird's wing bones, and there are claws on the digits. Simple peg-like teeth are present. The brain structure, as revealed by a cast from the interior of the skull, is similar to that of reptiles and quite different from that of birds, including later fossil birds.

In other features—some of its skull characters for example—*Archaeopteryx* seems to have been intermediate between certain pre-existing reptiles and modern flying birds. But in some characters it was typically avian, for example in those following. The clavicles are fused into a furcula or 'wishbone', a feature connected with the development and use of the wing. The pubic bones are slim and directed backwards, in connection with streamlining, abdominal support and the laying of large, hard-shelled

eggs. The distal tarsals and the metatarsal bones of the foot are fused into a tarsometatarsus, giving the extra unit peculiar to the leg of a bird. The big toe or hallux is opposable, for more efficient bipedal locomotion. And, most importantly, the structure of the feathers is indistinguishable from that of modern birds' plumage. Even the arrangement of feathers on the forearm is the same, with primaries borne on the hand and secondaries on the ulna.

Archaeopteryx thus provides a good example of an organism with some of its characteristics changing more quickly than others—the process known as mosaic evolution. The evolutionary distinction between reptile and bird must depend upon which

Reconstruction of *Archaeopteryx*.

characters are uniquely reptilian and which are avian, and which characters change first. *Archaeopteryx* had feathers—the outstanding and unique characteristic of members of the Aves. Therefore it was a bird; a very generalized bird, without the degree of specialization found in Aves today, but undoubtedly a bird.

What then did this first bird look like? The answer to this question depends not only on the animal's structure but also on its stance and behaviour. Fortunately, much can be seen in, or deduced from the fossil evidence.

It was about the size of a magpie—the common European and American magpies are about 18 in (45 cm) long—with rather similar proportions: long tail and somewhat

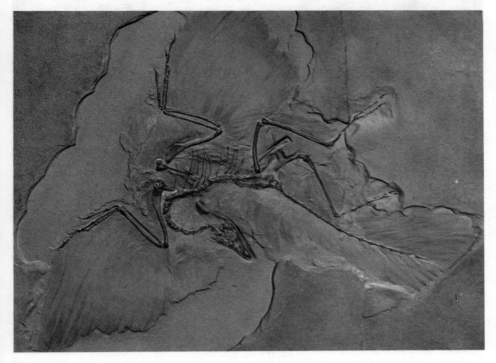

One of the two complete fossils of *Archaeopteryx*: even the imprint of the feathers can be seen.

Archaeopteryx, therefore, had a feather covering and general appearance similar to that of modern birds. Given a reduction of the free digits of the wing; with pectoral muscles supported by a keeled sternum; and with the unwieldy tail replaced by a fan of feathers, it would be little different from many birds living today. ORDER: Archaeopterygiformes, SUBCLASS: Archaeornithes, CLASS: Aves. P.M.D.

ARCHERFISH *Toxotes jaculatus* and related species, perciform fishes from southeast Asian freshwaters that shoot down insects with droplets of water. The archerfishes are small, rarely reaching more than 7 in (18 cm) in length in the wild. They have fairly deep bodies and the dorsal and anal fins are set far back near the tail. The body is generally silvery with three or four broad dark bars on the flanks.

The archerfishes live in muddy water and swim just below the surface searching for insects that rest on leaves overhanging the water. When a suitable insect is spotted, the

rounded wings. Dark brown pigment is present in the separate Bavarian feather specimen. We can tell from the opposable hind toe that the bird could have been quite active in trees, being able to grasp branches and therefore perch quite well. And undoubtedly the claws on the hand assisted in clambering around in trees and bushes. It is likely, therefore, that *Archaeopteryx* was aerial. But probably it could not fly actively, only glide. The reasons for this are fourfold. First of all there was no keel on the sternum for the attachment of the flight muscles, and the condition of other pectoral bones also indicates a poorly developed wing musculature. Secondly, the unspecialized nature of the hand skeleton indicates a relatively simple feather insertion and control with, consequently, a feeble wing-beat. Thirdly, the tail must have been too unwieldy to be used much in manoeuvring. And finally, the brain does not seem to have been sufficiently developed for the degree of co-ordination and control necessary for efficient flight.

But we must not assume that *Archaeopteryx* was clumsy or sluggish. Other gliding animals, 'flying' squirrels and 'flying' opossums for example, are very active and efficient in their own way and *Archaeopteryx* probably was too. In fact it may have been little different in general activity from birds such as the hoatzin. a relatively poor flier inhabiting the jungles bordering South American rivers, which, in the young stages, has claws on the digits for clambering around in branches.

Additional evidence for the efficiency of *Archaeopteryx* is that suggesting that it was

'warm-blooded' or, more properly speaking, had developed the means of maintaining its body temperature regardless of fluctuations in the temperature of its surroundings. This would have been made possible by its feather covering. From all the evidence it seems that feathers developed as an aid to temperature regulation some considerable time before true avian flight. It is quite likely that the *Archaeopteryx* stock was forced to take to the trees through competition with the many other vertebrates of like ecology which then flourished. And it could then have developed efficient flight by the elaboration of the already well-developed feather structure and support.

Archerfish *Toxotes jaculatus* and, above, showing how insect prey is brought down into the water.

Archerfish

fish pushes its snout out of the water and squirts droplets at the insect until it falls into the water and can be eaten. A small archerfish can only shoot a few inches but an adult can hit a fly up to 3 ft (90 cm) away. Their aim is remarkable when it is considered that their line of sight is diffracted as it passes from water to air. It has been found, however, that before 'shooting' an archerfish manoeuvres to place its body in as nearly a vertical line as possible, to minimize refraction. The jet of water is squirted between the tongue and the roof of the mouth. Along the tongue there is a ridge and above it a groove along the palate; water is forced through the narrow channel between the two and emerges as a fine stream.

Archerfishes will eat other foods if no insects are available, but they retain their shooting habits in the aquarium and can be trained to shoot for their food. They usually hit with the first shot but will alter their position in the water and try again if they fail. The act of shooting seems to be induced by hunger since a well-fed fish will not shoot whereas a hungry one will do so, even aiming at blemishes on the glass of the aquarium above the water-line. The force of the jet cannot be controlled with any accuracy. On occasions, if the jet is too powerful, the insect will be knocked out of reach so that it would seem that instinct rather than learned skill plays a major part in their shooting abilities. FAMILY: Toxotidae, ORDER: Perciformes, CLASS: Pisces.

ARCHERFISH, one of the most important things in any scientific work is to ensure that specimens are correctly labelled and identified. A single slip can cause immense confusion. The story of the discovery of the archerfish's ability to 'shoot' its prey provides an example of careless work. The first account of this behaviour was written in 1765 by the governor of a hospital in Java, then a Dutch colony. Unfortunately he sent his paper to Europe with a specimen of a butterflyfish. Consequently he was disbelieved because butterflyfishes live in the sea where there are no insects. It was not until 1902 when archerfishes were studied in an aquarium that the Dutch doctor was vindicated.

ARCHOSAURIA, a subclass of the Reptilia sometimes referred to as the 'Ruling reptiles' because of their dominance of the land faunas of the Mesozoic. The group comprises five orders: the Thecodontia from which all other archosaurs and birds evolved, the Saurischia and Ornithischia together including all dinosaurs, the Pterosauria which took to the air, and the Crocodilia.

In such a large and diverse group it is

Cynolebias nigripinnis, related to the Argentine pearlfish.

difficult to select diagnostic characters but archosaurs have in common a skull with two openings on each side behind the orbits for the passage of jaw muscles, and teeth that are set in sockets. Bipedal locomotion is a noted feature in several separate evolutionary lines and a number of forms are armoured. The group was primitively carnivorous but some descendant lines evolved herbivorous dentitions.

The archosaurs originated in the Permian, reached their zenith in the Mesozoic and then suffered wholesale extinction, the only order to survive into the Age of Mammals being the Crocodilia.

ARCTIC CHAR, an alternative name for the Alpine char *Salvelinus alpinus,* but a name that is also used in the United States for other species or races of char found in the cold arctic lakes of Canada and Alaska. FAMILY: Salmonidae, ORDER: Salmoniformes, CLASS: Pisces.

ARCTIC FAUNA, the environmental conditions and fauna of this area are dealt with under Polar faunas.

ARGENTINE PEARLFISH *Cynolebias belotti,* an egg-laying toothcarp from the La Plata basin in South America. All species of *Cynolebias* are annual fishes (see separate entry) and have a life span of only eight months, the adults dying while the eggs survive until the next season buried in the mud. The Argentine pearlfish, which grows to about $2\frac{1}{2}$ in (7 cm) in length, has a

moderately deep and stocky body. In the male, the back is a dark slaty blue and during the breeding season the underside is a deep emerald green. A series of vertical rows of white pearl-like spots cover the median fins and the tail. The female is duller in colour, with a yellow-brown body and irregular dark brown spots.

These are splendid fishes to keep in an aquarium (remembering always to get young ones since their life span is so short). Breeding is stimulated by gradually lowering the water-level in the tank. The courtship and deposition of eggs are interesting to watch since the pair burrow down into the substrate (peat is an ideal medium). After the eggs have been laid, the peat should be removed, placed in a small bowl and kept slightly moist. After some weeks the peat (and thus the eggs) should be replaced in the tank in slightly acid water and the young will hatch out fairly soon after. FAMILY: Cyprinodontidae, ORDER: Atheriniformes, CLASS: Pisces.

ARGENTINES, living in the midwaters of the North Atlantic. They resemble salmon and trout in having a small adipose fin behind the dorsal fin. Two species are occasionally trawled off European coasts, *Argentina silus* and *A. sphyraena.* The former is the larger of the two and reaches 2 ft (60 cm) in length. Its flesh is very palatable and it is known to live in shoals off the west coast of Ireland where it may in the future form the basis for an important fishery.

The name 'argentine' comes from the intensely silver colouring of these fishes, particularly in the form of a wide band down the flanks. FAMILY: Argentinidae, ORDER: Salmoniformes, CLASS: Pisces.

ARGONAUT, or *Paper nautilus, a cephalopod mollusc, the female of which secretes a papery shell-like structure with her tentacles.

This resembles the shell of the *Pearly nautilus in shape, hence the similarity of common names.

ARGUS, a name given to certain species of the marine perch-like fishes known as grouper. The Blue-spotted argus *Cephalopholis argus* is perhaps the best known. It is found in the tropical Pacific and reaches a maximum length of 18 in (46 cm). The body is brown or olive passing into a deep blue on the fins with many small light blue spots edged with darker blue over both body and fins. There are also four to six whitish circular bands around the body, but these fishes are renowned for their quick colour changes and the bands will appear and disappear in rapid succession. The Blue-spotted argus has now been introduced into Hawaiian waters where it was previously unknown. FAMILY: Serranidae, ORDER: Perciformes, CLASS: Pisces.

ARISTOTLE, 384–322 BC, has pre-eminent claim to title of 'Father of Zoology'. Born in Macedonia into a long line of court physicians and raised in a learned atmosphere, at the age of 18 he entered Plato's Academy in Athens where he remained for 20 years. Becoming opposed to Plato's teaching and being passed over as his successor, he moved in 347 to Asia Minor to the court of a small king, whose daughter he married. In 342, after a civil revolt, he returned to Macedonia where for three years he was tutor to Alexander, the future conqueror. He then moved back to Athens in a position of great authority, setting up the Lycaeum, the archetype of learned foundations. For 12 years Aristotle taught in Athens until the death of Alexander and further political intrigue forced him to flee to the island of Euboea where he died shortly afterwards.

Aristotle's industry and output were prodigious, and apart from his pre-eminence as a biologist he has had considerable influence in the fields of metaphysics, art and statesmanship. None of his original writings remains, but generally regarded as Aristotle's work are ten books *On the History of Animals,* five books *On the Reproduction of Animals,* four books *On the Parts of Animals,* three books *On the Soul,* and two books concerned with movements. Altogether he refers to 520 different species of animals known today. His classification of animals was in the form of the first 'Scala Natura', with different types being arranged in ascending order of complexity according to the type of 'spirit' they possessed (the last 'Scala Natura' was that of Buffon in the 18th century). Aristotle also considered such topics as heredity, sex and growth, and he did excellent work in embryology. Some of his ideas were primitive and he accepted too freely the statements of others, but his personal work was brilliant, some of it waiting for confirmation for over 2,000 years. He was even approaching a theory of evolution in the modern sense.   P.M.D.

ARK SHELLS, bivalve molluscs belonging to the large and widely distributed family Arcidae. They are primitive insofar as the gill filaments are not united to one another by tissue junctions as in higher bivalves. The hinge mechanism is also unspecialized; there are some 40–50 similar tiny teeth arranged along a straight hinge line rather than a few more complex interlocking teeth as in higher bivalves. There are about 150 species of Ark shells and they tend to be commonest in warm seas from low water down to 1500 ft (500 m) depth. European species include *Arca tetragona, A. lactea* and *A. pectunculoides.* The former reaches 1½ in (3·9 cm) in length and is widespread but not common on rocky shores and amongst crevices. It is also found below the low water mark and is firmly attached to the substratum by green byssus threads secreted by a special gland on the foot. Both *Arca lactea* and *A. pectunculoides* occur below low water mark and are commonest to the south and west of the British Isles. One of the larger Ark shells is the Bloody clam *Arca pexata* which has a shell 2–3 in (5–7½ cm) long and which occurs on the Coast of North America, from Rhode Island to Georgia. In common with *Arca inflata* and the Noah's ark shell, the Bloody clam has the respiratory pigment haemoglobin which is confined within corpuscles very similar to those occurring in vertebrates. In *A. inflata* the blood corpuscles are 0·015 mm thick and 0·018–0·021 mm in diameter and contain a nucleus with a diameter 0·005 mm.

The Noah's ark shell *A. noae* is another large species which reaches 3–5 in (7·5–12·5 cm) in length. It occurs in the Mediterranean and from North Carolina to the West Indies; as in *A. tetragona,* the Noah's ark shell is

Nine-banded armadillo, typical of all members of its family.

attached to the substratum by means of byssus threads. Unlike the threads of mussels, however, the byssus of the Ark shells hardens after secretion to form a cone-like structure composed of horny plates. As in the mussels, the byssus can be detached and resecreted rapidly. Other species of Ark shell include *A. americana* and *A. incongrua* which occur from North Carolina to the West Indies; *A. traversa* which lives off the coast of New England and *A. reticulata* which is a warm water species living off the coast of S. California and in the West Indies. Many species of *Arca* and related genera occur in the waters of Australia; common genera from this region include *Bathyarca, Barbatia* and *Anadara*. FAMILY: Arcidae, ORDER: Fili-branchia, CLASS: Bivalvia, PHYLUM: Mollusca. R.C.N.

ARMADILLO, the only armoured mammal, related to the sloths and anteaters, and all belonging to the order Edentata. The family, Dasypodidae, contains nine groups or genera and about 20 species that vary in size from the Giant anteater *Priodontes giganteus,* weighing as much as 132 lb (60 kg) and reaching almost 5 ft (150 cm) in overall length, to the tiny 5 in (12·7 cm) Fairy armadillo or pichiciago *Chlamy-phorus truncatus.*

Armadillo armour is remarkably modified skin in the form of horny bands and plates connected by flexible tissue that enables the animal to move and bend its body. Narrow bands across the back break the rigidity of the armour there, and their number (characteristic of the genus) is often useful for identification as reflected in some of the common names such as Nine-banded, Six-banded and Three-banded armadillos. The underparts of these edentates are covered with soft-haired skin, and in many armadillos hair projects either between the bands or from under the side plates and legs. The hairs are greyish brown to white in colour, and the armour is brown to pinkish. Most of the armadillos can draw their legs and feet beneath the shell and a few, but not many, can roll into a ball. The Three-banded armadillo *Tolypeutes,* of the Argentine pampas, however, is the only one that can completely close up into a perfect sphere, snapping the shell shut like a steel trap. As a result of the armour armadillos are heavy animals. They are reputed to be able to walk on the bottom of ponds and other bodies of water, but they are also good swimmers.

Armadillos have small ears, an extensible tongue, relatively good senses of sight, smell and hearing, and strong claws on the forefeet. Although the name of the order means 'without teeth', only the anteaters are toothless. Sloths and armadillos possess teeth but they are all molars. Armadillos have the most, normally 14 to 18 in each jaw, but the

Giant armadillo may have a combined total of 80 to 100. Armadillo teeth are among the most primitive found in mammals, being simply peg-shaped blocks of dentine without enamel, and they grow continuously at the roots.

The numerous species of armadillos range from southern Kansas and Florida to Patagonia. Most live in Brazil, Bolivia and Argentina, and while they are popularly associated with rocky arid regions, armadillos actually are found in a variety of habitats from pampas and savannahs to marshes and dense forests. Only one group, the Nine-banded armadillo *Dasypus,* reaches North America. During the past century these aliens have gradually extended their range north and east in the United States—across Texas to Kansas and Missouri. But their expansion is limited by the freezing line for armadillos cannot endure low temperatures. They have been introduced into Florida.

In the armadillos polyembryony (the production of two or more identical offspring

Armadillo's digging claw.

from the division of a single fertilized ovum) commonly occurs. Species of armadillos may give birth to as many as 12 young from a single fertilized egg, but the usual number per litter is two to four, and often only one embryo survives. The Nine-banded armadillo *Dasypus novemcinctus,* typically gives birth to quadruplets. Delayed implantation often obscures the true gestation period, but in the Nine-banded species birth occurs about 120 days after implantation or up to 260 days after mating. Armadillo young at birth are covered with soft leathery skin that gradually hardens into the armour of the species.

Powerful diggers and scratchers, armadillos forage and root for a variety of food: insects and other arthropods, worms, eggs, small reptiles and amphibians, fruits, leaves and shoots, and even carrion. They generally walk on the tips of the claws and the entire soles of the feet. Most can run rapidly. Some, such as Nine-banded armadillos, have become agricultural pests in certain areas, but the animals in general destroy many injurious insects and a number of venomous snakes. Armadillos are found singly, in pairs, or occasionally in small groups. They may be nocturnal or diurnal, and their home is an

underground burrow dug with their claws or one abandoned by other animals. Some armadillos are quite vocal. Nine-bandeds, for example, grunt almost constantly while rooting about in their nervous, jerky fashion, and one of the Hairy armadillos *Chaetophractus villosus* snarls when disturbed. Armadillos can fight with their claws, but their first reaction is to run to the safety of their burrows or dig rapidly into the ground and anchor themselves in the soil. If caught before accomplishing either, they draw in their feet or curl into a ball. The flesh of some, notably Hairy and Nine-banded armadillos and pichis *Zaedyus pichi,* is highly palatable, and these species are often systematically hunted. Maximum captive life spans of armadillos vary from six and a half years for the Nine-banded to almost 16 years for the Hairy. FAMILY: Dasypodidae, ORDER: Edentata, CLASS: Mammalia. M.M.W.

ARMADILLO ADVANCE, the spread of the Nine-banded armadillo northwards into the United States is surprising because the armadillo family is in general showing signs of decline. The reason for the spread is not known but it has been well documented. In 1880 the Nine-banded armadillo did not live very far north of the United States-Mexico border. By 1905 it had reached the Colorado River and the spread continued northward until the climate became too severe.

In its spread the armadillo has met a new enemy—the motor car. Its chances of being run over are increased by its habit of leaping into the air when alarmed and so being hit by the car's body.

ARMYWORMS, term given to the caterpillars of some moths, which sometimes appear in enormous numbers and, after having exhausted local food supplies, migrate in vast armies to new areas. The most important species is *Leucania unipuncta,* occurring in North America, Australia and elsewhere, but several species of *Laphygma* have the same habit.

Leucania unipuncta feeds mainly on grasses and grain crops and the caterpillars may do enormous damage. For instance, in an outbreak in 1953 it is estimated that in Kentucky alone armyworms ate about $3,500,000 worth of crops. Most of this damage is done by the last stage larvae which are up to 2 in (5 cm) long. They can be controlled with insecticides and, when they are migrating, new crops can be protected by digging a ditch across their line of march. The caterpillars are unable to climb up the steep sides of the ditch and accumulate in the deeper parts. They can then be destroyed by pouring diesel oil over them.

The adult moth to which an armyworm

gives rise is a rather nondescript looking pale brown insect with a wing-span of about $1\frac{1}{2}$ in (3·8 cm). The adults migrate as well as the caterpillars and such adult migrations, occurring unseen at night, may partly account for the sudden upsurges of army-worms in areas in which they had not previously been common. An adult female lays up to 2,000 eggs in batches of 25—100 and the young caterpillars hatch in a week or so. In Canada there are only two generations each year, the partly grown larvae of the second generation overwintering hidden at the bases of plants, but in the warmer south development may be continuous with five or more generations in a year. With a breeding rate as high as this plague numbers can appear in a very short time. ORDER: Lepidoptera, CLASS: Insecta, PHYLUM: Arthropoda.

AROUSAL. Observation of animals leads us to the conclusion that at times they are indifferent to what goes on around them, while at others they are attentive and are spurred into action. This arousal is shown in the animal's movements, such as pricking of the ears to catch a sound or following a moving object with the eyes. With the change of behaviour comes a change in the electrical activity of the brain, much of which takes place in the reticular formation. Each stimulus falling on a sense organ gives rise to two kinds of response in the brain. One is in the area particularly responsible for that sense, for example, the visual cortex for vision, the other is more general and arises from all tracts carrying incoming sensory impulses. These are fed to the reticular formation and so to the higher centres and 'arouse' them into action. In this way a stimulus may change the animal's responsiveness to other stimuli. It is being discovered that parts of the brain in lower vertebrates and in invertebrates have a similar function to the reticular formation of mammals.

Arrow-worms *Sagitta elegans*.

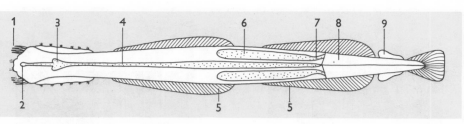

Anatomy of arrow-worm: 1. head bristles, 2. mouth, 3. gullet, 4. intestine, 5. fin, 6. ovary, 7. oviduct, 8. testis, 9. vesicula seminalis.

The need for sensory inflow to keep the nervous system 'topped up', as it were, is well known in human beings who are seriously upset psychologically if they are placed, weightless, in the dark and in silence. A simple example which helps us to understand this may be seen in insects. The ocelli, or simple eyes on the top of an insect's head, seem to mediate few responses directly but their stimulation by light is essential for other responses to take place. Blackening the ocelli may reverse the insect's response to light, turning one which takes it towards the light into one which makes it shun the light. It may also result in a general immobility of the insect. Thus sensory input seems to be essential for the general arousal of the animal.

Arousal of tendencies to attack, escape or behave sexually are linked with endocrine changes. Indeed the outward signs of these tendencies are produced by hormones released into the bloodstream. The adrenal medulla releases adrenalin which causes increased heart-beat, the erection of hair, increased secretion of the sweat glands, rapid and deep breathing and the diversion of blood from the gut to the muscles. This has been called the 'flight, fight and fright' syndrome. The changes prepare the body for violent action. Such an aroused state, if long lasting, imposes considerable stress on the body. But the secretion of the adreno-cortico-trophic hormone (ACTH) by the pituitary under the influence of the hypothalamus helps the animal to adapt to the stress.

Generally the following pattern can be traced. Incoming stimuli rouse the higher centre via the reticular formation and the animal pays attention. If the stimulation continues, brain activity influences the hypothalamus which initiates, through the pituitary, the secretion of adrenalin and the animal is 'roused' and may show what we choose to call 'emotion'. Finally, very persistent stimulation producing stress will initiate ACTH secretion and the animal adapts to the stress.   J.D.C.

ARROW-WORMS, small worm-like marine animals belonging to one genus and important because they indicate the movements of sea water. Their entire lives are spent drifting. Like all planktonic animals their swimming speed is less than the movements of the sea around them and they are transported long distances, mostly in the surface waters, though three species are carried in deep oceanic currents. Arrow-worms are torpedo-

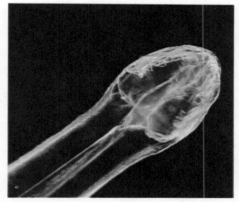

Close-up of head of *Sagitta setosa*.

shaped and usually less than $\frac{1}{2}$ in (1 cm) long, the largest of them, *Sagitta maxima*, reaching 2 in (5 cm).

Apart from the head and the posterior reproductive region, the arrow-worm is largely transparent. The body is flattened with thin lateral extensions or fins and a horizontal tail fin. On either side of the mouth there are hook-like bristles which are used as jaws; hence the name of the phylum to which it belongs: Chaetognatha, from the Greek *chaete* (hair or bristles) and *gnathos* (jaw). The transparent body permits an all-round vision through spherical eyes, befitting an

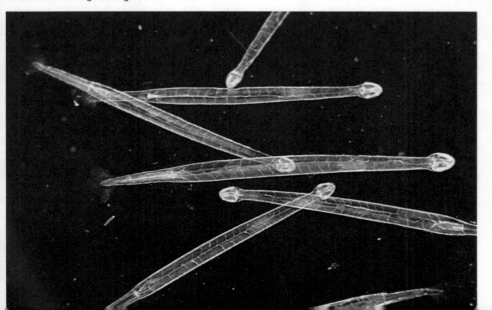

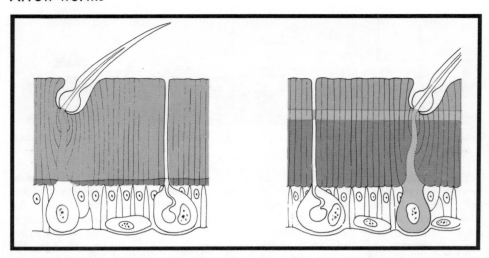

Section through cuticle (coloured) and hypodermis of an insect, with a sensory bristle. To right, a nerve-cell (green) connects with the base of a bristle. (see Arthropoda)

animal living in suspension and surrounded by both food and predators.

Arrow-worms feed on other animals of the *plankton by suddenly darting like an arrow towards their prey with a quick up and down flip of the tail. Yet, though capable of these sudden bursts of speed, they are truly planktonic. Animals of similar size are seized with the jaws and swallowed whole. At certain times of the year arrow-worms are responsible for great mortality among developing fish fry. In their turn they are consumed by larger predators of the plankton including jellyfishes and comb-jellies, as well as by plankton-eating fishes such as herrings.

Arrow-worms are hermaphrodite, the ovary lying in front of the testes. These are connected with a bulge in the body surface behind the lateral fins where sperm can be stored. The male gonads mature first. Either cross-fertilization with another individual occurs or the sperm is stored until the eggs have matured when self-fertilization takes place. In the deep-water Eukronia hamata the lateral fins form a brood pouch under the body. First the eggs and then the young are carried in it. Surface arrow-worms of the Antarctic move into deeper water to breed.

Marine biologists and hydrographers throughout the world use the various species of arrow-worms to trace the movements of sea water, especially the origins of coastal and off-shore waters to determine the pattern of water movements over the continental shelf. This is possible because of the distinctive tolerances of the different species. Thus each species of Sagitta has preferences in regard to temperature, salt content or depth of water beneath it. For example, S. arctica is confined to very cold water, whereas S. hexaptera and S. enflata are tropical. S. maxima is another cold water form, but one which will tolerate warmer conditions.

When the Arctic arrow-worm is found in plankton hauls in the northern half of the North Sea, it means that there has been a southerly flow of water from the Norwegian Sea into the area. Similarly, the presence of S. lyra in the North Sea indicates that water from the Mediterranean has passed to the west of the British Isles and entered the North Sea. When S. serratodentata is present, it signifies that oceanic water has come in from the mid-Atlantic. The whole route of the Gulf Stream, or North Atlantic Drift, is demonstrated by the distribution of S. serratodentata. It is taken in the Gulf of Maine, U.S.A., and as the bulk of the water passes to the northeast across the Atlantic, large numbers are collected over deeper water off the south-western approaches of the British Isles, in the latter half of the year. Some of the water escapes south to the Azores, whilst its passage northwards is indicated when this species of arrow-worms is taken off Iceland and in the Norwegian, Barentsz and North Seas later in the year.

The arrow-worms S. setosa and S. elegans are found in temperate waters over a continental shelf, S. elegans occuring off Canadian, American and European coasts, while S. setosa is European. Differences in the water preferences of these two species provide further information concerning the hydrography of the British Isles. S. setosa is indigenous to the English Channel and the North Sea but is absent when a mixture of oceanic water has taken place. It is collected at all times of the year in the narrower eastern part of the English Channel and in the southern half of the North Sea, indicating that these partially land locked areas do not receive oceanic water.

S. elegans occurs only where there is a mixing of coastal and oceanic water and is therefore found off the west and northeast coasts of the British Isles at certain times of the year. Its presence in the northern half of the North Sea in late autumn is further confirmation of the inflow of Atlantic water. demonstrate the presence of warm water and S. maxima indicates an inflow of colder arctic

water. Although these arrow-worms tolerate being transported to cooler or warmer waters, they are unable to breed under these conditions and their seasonal appearance is followed by death, a factor contributing to their value as indicators.

For reasons which are not completely understood, where mixing of coastal and oceanic water occurs in shallow seas there is a rich plankton. This is accompanied by high concentrations of essential minerals and salts and relatively large numbers of young fishes (excluding very young herring). Further, when young fishes are reared in the laboratory in this water, improved survival rates are S. elegans also lives and breeds in the Gulf of Maine on the northeastern seaboard of the United States indicating mixing of masses of water from different sources in this area. S. serratodentata and S. lyra in the area obtained. The presence of S. elegans is indicative of these conditions. So although a relatively insignificant member of the whole plankton, it is associated with water masses containing a rich plankton and, correspondingly, large commercial fisheries. Indeed, the density of S. elegans is directly correlated with the numbers of herring present in the North Sea, a statistic of value to commercial fisheries. PHYLUM: Chaetognatha.

W.A.M.C.

ARROW-WORMS. In the study of oceanography frequent use is made of indicator species, that is, species that are characteristic of a particular water-mass and allow scientists to identify the mass without resorting to lengthy chemical tests. Two such species are the arrow-worms Sagitta elegans and S. setosa. The former is characteristic of water that is rich in plankton, has abundant phosphate in winter and contains some substance that promotes the growth of planktonic larvae. Water containing S. setosa is poor in plankton and lacks the unknown growth substance. The two arrow-worms are so characteristic of their water-masses that it is possible to put a ship across the boundary of the masses, and catch one species from the bows and the other from the stern.

Sagitta elegans and S. setosa are convenient indicator species because they can easily be told apart. S. elegans becomes opaque if dropped into formalin preservative while S. setosa remains transparent. From 1924 onwards sea water in the English Channel off Plymouth has been regularly sampled and in 1931 it was found that the setosa water in the Channel was moving westwards to push the boundary with the Atlantic elegans water westwards. A few years later the local winter herring fishery declined and died out as the herring were unable to survive in the less rich setosa water.

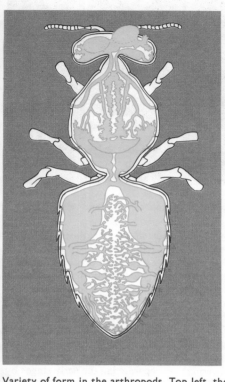

Diagram showing the air-sacs in a worker honey-bee, indicating how these communicate with the exterior.

ARTERY, a blood vessel which carries blood away from the heart. In vertebrates the arteries have thick walls, containing fibrous and muscular layers, able to withstand the high pressures at which blood leaves the heart. Those invertebrates which have blood systems generally only develop low blood pressures and their arteries, if present, are usually quite thin-walled.

ARTHRODIRES, an order of fossil fishes belonging to the class Placodermi. See Fossil fishes and fishes, classification. ORDER: Arthrodira, CLASS: Placodermi.

ARTHROPLEURIDS, an extinct group of arthropods probably related to the centipedes and millipedes. They inhabited coal swamps during Upper Carboniferous (Pennsylvanian) times and grew up to 6 ft (1·8 m) in length, which makes them the largest known land arthropods.

The head was small and its structure is poorly known. The body, long and flattened, contained at least 27 segments, the exact number being unknown. Its upper surface had a pair of shallow grooves running the whole length, one on each side of the midline, marking off each segment into a middle and two lateral lobes. This gives a superficial resemblance to the trilobites which misled some early workers on this group. On its lower surface each segment bore a pair of simple, jointed legs with short claws.

The arthropleurids fed on plants including club mosses. PHYLUM: Arthropoda.

ARTHROPODA, the largest and most diverse phylum in the animal kingdom. It includes, among others, the millipedes, centipedes, insects, crustaceans, Horseshoe crabs, arachnids and Sea spiders. The fundamental characteristics that these have in common are a segmented exoskeleton with jointed limbs, a ventral nerve cord and a dorsal heart. Sometimes the limbs are absent, sometimes the heart is absent and sometimes the nerve cord is condensed to a solid mass, but the exoskeleton is always present. Sometimes the

Variety of form in the arthropods. Top left, the centipede shows best the typically segmented body and jointed limbs, as does the millipede top right, in the Lepidoptera, bottom left, the body is shortened, there are six legs and two pairs of wings, while in the spider, bottom right, there are eight legs and no wings.

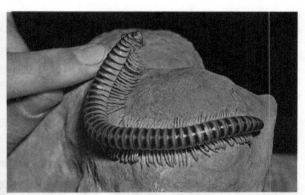

Common lobster, an arthropod with appendages modified for different functions. Note the differences between the antennae, claws and walking legs.

exoskeleton is extremely thin and flexible, more often it is relatively massive, with flexible joints between rigid plates.

The exoskeleton of arthropods is not just a protection against mechanical injury, it also prevents loss of water from land-dwelling arthropods. Its structure is complex. Over the epidermis are layers of chitin, which is a fairly flexible substance, but may be toughened in one of two ways to form hard plates. One way, found in the Crustacea and the milli-pedes, is for the chitin to be impregnated with lime salts. This reaches its peak in the hard exoskeletons of the larger crabs. The other way, found in all arthropods to some extent, is for the chitin to be impregnated with a protein, which is then tanned by substances called quinones to give a hard brown or black substance called sclerotin. Any part that has undergone this process is said to be sclerotized.

The outer layers of the exoskeleton are very thin, and vary in details from one group of arthropods to another. These layers are responsible in land-dwelling arthropods for waterproofing the exoskeleton. In some insects there are four layers with a total thickness of only 0·004 mm. The most important of these layers from a waterproof-ing point of view is a thin layer of wax which varies from one insect to another. Insects living in hot dry places have a wax which functions best as a waterproofing agent at higher temperatures than the wax from insects living in cooler, damper places.

Arthropods vary in the efficiency of their waterproofing. In some of the woodlice the exoskeleton allows a fairly rapid loss of water. But woodlice spend most of their time in damp places, so their losses of water are likely to be low. If they do wander out into the sun the rapid evaporation of water keeps them cool and may prevent their bodies from reaching a lethal temperature. As soon as a woodlouse begins to lose water rapidly it moves to a dark damp place, and remains there. In this case the lack of waterproof layer seems to be an adaptation to cool the animal by evaporation if it is exposed to short periods of high temperature.

The presence of a rigid exoskeleton poses certain problems in relation to growth. The flexible parts can stretch to some extent, but for any major increase in size to take place the exoskeleton must be cast off at intervals. This process is known as moulting. Before an arthropod moults it lays down a new soft exoskeleton beneath the old one. The two coverings are separated in the early stages by a fluid which digests away part of the old exoskeleton. In the later stages the old exoskeleton splits along predetermined lines and the arthropod forces its way out. Often there is a rapid and dramatic increase in size after moulting. The arthropod swells by taking water and stretches the new soft exoskeleton. While the exoskeleton is soft the arthropod is vulnerable to attack, and many forms that are normally pugnacious, such as crabs, become shy and retiring, hiding in holes or under stones until the new exo-skeleton has hardened.

The process of moulting is controlled by glandular secretions. These have been studied best in insects and crustaceans. In both groups a gland in the thorax secretes a hormone that stimulates the onset of moult-ing. The details of other hormones that influence moulting, growth and maturation vary from one group to another, but most arthropods have several glandular regions in their nervous systems. The products from these regions often travel along nerves and are released at points some distance from the site of production. A major release point is in the eyestalks of crabs and shrimps.

In general insects cease moulting once they have become adult, but many crustaceans continue moulting throughout life, although there are some whole subclasses, such as the Copepoda which cease moulting once they have become sexually mature.

The muscles of arthropods are of necessity attached to the inside of the exoskeleton. Often there are special thickenings and internal projections (apodemes) for the attachment of muscles. When a muscle is particularly powerful its insertion into the

One of the most primitive arthropods still alive, the Horseshoe or King crab.

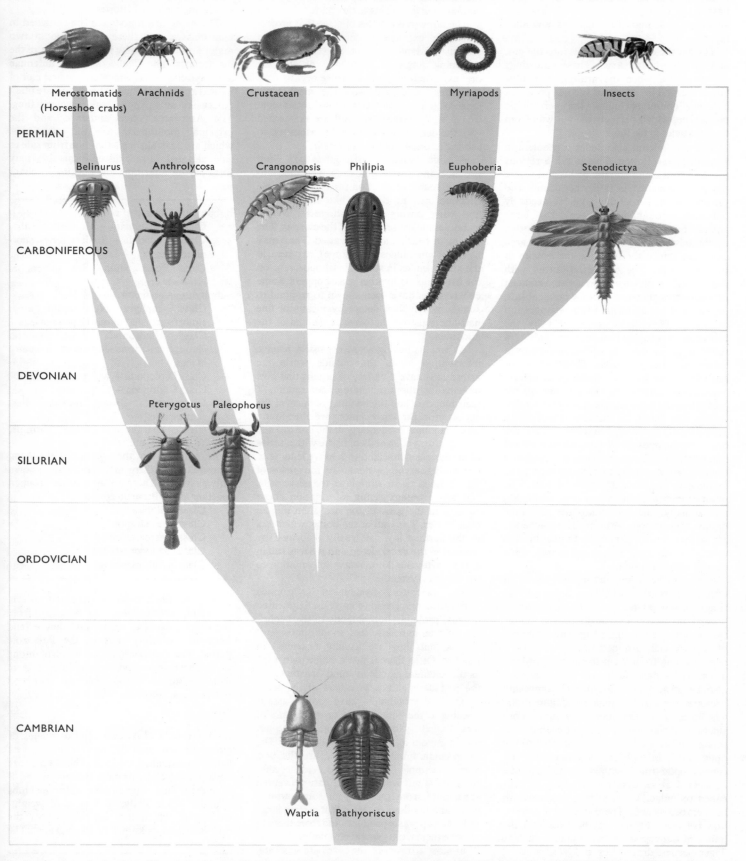

Merostomatids   Arachnids   Crustacean   Myriapods   Insects
(Horseshoe crabs)

PERMIAN

Belinurus   Anthrolycosa   Crangonopsis   Philipia   Euphoberia   Stenodictya

CARBONIFEROUS

DEVONIAN

Pterygotus   Paleophorus

SILURIAN

ORDOVICIAN

CAMBRIAN

Waptia   Bathyoriscus

Evolution of the Arthropoda. The earliest known forms were the trilobites, from which sprang the Sea scorpions (left centre), which led to the Horse-shoe crab (top left). Other lines led to the spiders, crabs, millipedes and insects living today.

exoskeleton takes the form of fibres which pass right through the epidermis and are anchored well into the thickened chitinous layers.

The exoskeleton also extends into the gut, at both mouth and anus. These intuckings are also shed when the arthropod moults. Often the middle region of the gut produces its own chitinous lining, the peritrophic membrane, which protects the gut wall from hard particles in the food.

The exoskeleton also poses a problem in relation to respiration. This is not a serious problem to a small aquatic arthropod where the outer covering is fairly permeable and the animal can get all the oxygen it needs by diffusion through its surface. The large aquatic forms develop gills, which are often elaborately frilled to increase the surface area and have thin walls to make the uptake of oxygen easier. The terrestrial forms with waterproof cuticles are faced with the greatest problem: how they can become permeable to oxygen without allowing a fatal evaporation of water. They have solved this by the evolution of the tracheal system. This is a series of tubes, opening at the surface by a limited number of pores. These pores, or spiracles, often have an elaborate structure, with special closing muscles and devices for preventing the entry of dust and other foreign bodies. The tubes, or tracheae, ramify with progressively smaller branches to all the organs of the body. In its most elaborate form the tracheal system involves air sacs and tracheal trunks through which air is pumped by muscular movement of the abdomen. The finest branches of the system, the tracheoles, may actually penetrate some of the cells of the organs they supply with air. The tracheoles are so fine that air cannot be forced through them, so the final stages of supply must depend upon diffusion.

The most conspicuous sense organs of an arthropod are usually its eyes. These may be simple or compound, and both types may be present in the same arthropod. The simple eyes usually have a single lens with a number of sensory cells grouped underneath and a nerve leading from them to the brain. Many larval forms have such eyes and they may also be present in adult forms. Compound eyes are composed of units called ommatidia. The structure of the ommatidia shows considerable variation in detail, but each can be thought of as a tubular eye connected to the optic nerve. In each ommatidium there is a central optic tract, with a crystalline cone connected at its base with a group of cells called retinulae. These in turn connect with the nervous system. There is often a correlation between the size of the eyes and the habits of arthropods. Active hunters, such as Tiger beetles, dragonflies and Wolf spiders, usually have large eyes. Some deepsea crustaceans also have large eyes, but those that live in total darkness often lack eyes, as do many cave-dwelling arthropods.

The numerous bristles or setae that project from the exoskeleton of arthropods are variously adapted to act as sense organs, grooming organs, weapons, or feeding organs. When they act as sense organs they are often concerned with the mechanical sense of touch. Some thin walled setae seem to be highly permeable, and are concerned with the detection of chemical substances, so serving as organs of taste or smell.

A wide range of arthropods can both produce and perceive sounds. The mechanisms of sound production range from simple frictional rasping devices, like the hind legs and wing covers of grasshoppers, to the elaborate muscular drums of the cicadas. The organs of hearing are also varied. They may be on the antennules, as in some Crustacea, in the abdomen, as in some grasshoppers, or on the front legs, as in other grasshoppers. Some cockroaches have been shown to respond to sounds which they detect by means of fine hair-like setae on the cerci at the end of the abdomen.

As well as having sense organs to receive information about the outside world the arthropods have a variety of organs that give information about the state of contraction of their muscles, and the bending of parts of the exoskeleton. Stretch receptors are often found near the joints, particularly in the limbs. They take the form of strands of tissue with a series of nerve cells connected to a nerve leading to the central nervous system. Any movement of the strand of tissue stimulates the nerve cells. The sense organs giving information about stresses in the exoskeleton are often minute oval domes. The wall of the dome, which lies in the surface layer, is easily deformed by stresses in the exoskeleton and a nerve cell in contact with the dome relays information to the nervous system.

The execretory system of arthropods varies from one group to another. Segmented organs, probably homologous to the nephridia of the annelids, are found in several groups, but they are usually restricted in number. Often there is just a single pair, such as the antennal glands in some Crustacea, or the maxillary glands in others of the same class. The arachnids have coxal glands opening at the bases of one or more pairs of legs. Excretory organs opening into the gut are common in terrestrial arthropods. The Malpighian tubules of insects are the best known example. There is also evidence that the general gut wall can eliminate unwanted substances from the body in some arthropods, and in others it seems that certain large cells take up waste products and store them to remove them from general circulation.

In most arthropods the sexes are separate, but a few forms particularly among the Crustacea are hermaphrodites, and several shrimps and woodlice are known to change sex during their life histories.

The living arthropods can be classified in nine classes, and these are placed in two major groups according to the structure of the mouthparts. The Chelicerata lack antennae and have chelicerae, which are the first pair of jointed appendages on the head, and are often pincer-like or equipped with a poison fang. The Antennata have antennae, and the principal mouthparts are the mandibles, which are basically jaws that bite from side to side, although in specialized forms they may form part of a piercing and sucking mechanism.

Subphylum Chelicerata
    Class Merostomata – Horseshoe crabs
    Class Arachnida – Spiders, mites, scorpions, etc.
    Class Pycnogonida – Sea spiders or No-body crabs
Subphylum Antennata
    Class Symphyla – No common name: small forms with about 12 pairs of legs
    Class Pauropoda – No common name: small forms with about nine pairs of legs
    Class Diplopoda – Millipedes
    Class Chilopoda – Centipedes
    Class Insecta – Insects, including flies, beetles, ants, etc.
    Class Crustacea – Crabs, shrimps, Water fleas, etc.

In addition to the classes with living representatives there are five classes known only as fossils. These are sometimes grouped together as the Proarthropoda.
    Class Trilobita
    Class Merostomoidea
    Class Marrelomorpha
    Class Pseudocrustacea
    Class Arthropleurida

Of these the Trilobita are the best known. Numerous species have been described from the older geological strata, and they extend back to the early part of the Paleozoic period. The Pseudocrustacea are also among the earliest arthropod fossils, being known from the Burgess Shales, which are estimated to have been laid down over 400 million years ago.   Ja.G.

ARTIODACTYLA, even-toed ungulates or cloven-hoofed animals, one of the largest living mammalian orders. The hoofs are analogous to claws or nails around the end of each digit. They provide support for the limbs and the whole body. The type of weight-bearing in which the toes alone bear the body's weight, is known as 'digitigrade'. The

Dall's sheep of North America.

Hippopotamuses and (below) their relatives, domestic pigs.

'plantigrade' type is that in which the whole surface of the foot is placed flat on the ground. The particular digitigrade type of locomotion in which the tip of the terminal phalanx, supported by a hoof, rests on the ground is known as 'unguligrade' and is the extreme in running adaptations. Since the foot must be lightened in weight while remaining firm, all subsidiary toes are lost, leaving just one or two central toes to bear the whole weight of each limb.

The difference between the Artiodactyla and Perissodactyla is that in the former the weight is borne equally on two central toes, while in the latter there is only a single toe to bear the weight. The two weight-bearing digits of artiodactyls are numbers three and four. In some forms digits two and five are also still present, but small and often not normally touching the ground. They are referred to as lateral or false hoofs, or dew-claws. In those artiodactyls in which they are present, they tend to function in some way, for instance as stabilizers in climbing up

slopes. No artiodactyl is known in which the first digit is present.

Not all living artiodactyls are runners. Some have become secondarily rather slow-moving, even ponderous animals and these tend to have the largest lateral hoofs and to rest part of their weight on them. The same thing has occurred in some perissodactyls. The resemblance between the artiodactyl hippopotamus and the perissodactyl rhinoceros is more than just a matter of names: both are ungulates which have begun to specialize as runners, but have 'slowed down' during the course of evolution, becoming ponderous and retaining large lateral toes to spread their weight. Also, since they can no longer protect themselves by fleeing from their enemies, they have both acquired a thick skin for protection.

Other running specializations are seen in the Artiodactyla. The forearm bones (radius and ulna) and shin bones (tibia and fibula) have fused, strengthening and lightening the limb. The limb segments tend to increase in length, the radius being longer than the

humerus and the tibia longer than the femur. The humerus and femur are beneath the skin of the trunk and the free portion of the limb begins with the radius and tibia respectively. The 'knee' of the forelimb is in fact the wrist, and the cannon bone is a fusion of metacarpals three and four while the 'hock' of the hindlimb is the tarsus, and the shannon bone, or shank, is a fusion of metatarsals three and four. The talus, the tarsal bone which articulates with the tibia, is a highly characteristic shape, with a rolling surface above and a pulley surface below: in perissodactyls it has a pulley surface above only and is flat below.

The teeth are specialized for grass-eating: the molar cusps are united into hard-wearing ridges and there is much cement on the grinding surfaces. The upper incisors are reduced or absent and there is a gap, the diastema, between the lower canines and the cheekteeth. The dental formula is $\frac{0-3\ 0-1\ 2-4\ 3}{1-3\ 0-1\ 2-4\ 3}$ =32-44.

Since these are herbivores always on the lookout for danger and running from pre-

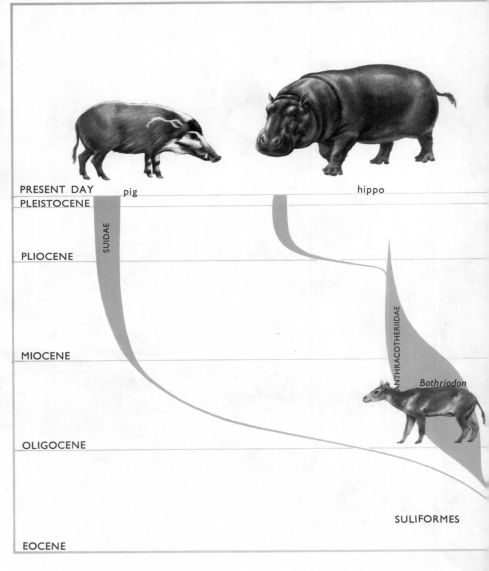

PRESENT DAY   pig   hippo
PLEISTOCENE

PLIOCENE

SUIDAE

MIOCENE

ANTHRACOTHERIIDAE   *Bothriodon*

OLIGOCENE

SULIFORMES

EOCENE

dators, they need a digestive system which enables them to get as much food as possible inside them in a short space of time in case they are interrupted and have to flee. And yet vegetable food needs far more digestion than does meat. Accordingly, artiodactyls have a complex stomach divided into several compartments, of which the first, the rumen or 'paunch', only possessed by the suborder Pecora, is a storage chamber like a bird's crop. Food is swallowed and remains in the rumen and at a later time, when the animal is at its leisure, the food is regurgitated into its mouth and well masticated, undergoing salivary digestion known as rumination. The other compartments—three in the Pecora—are the reticulum or 'honeycomb', the psalterium or 'manyplies' and the abomasum or 'reed'. Each has a different digestive function, but the main process goes on in the abomasum.

The penis of artiodactyls is fibroelastic in type, not dependant on vascularization or frictional stimulation: hence copulation takes only a second or two—another open-country

adaptation related to the need for speedy retreat.

The order Artiodactyla is classified into three suborders and ten families, as follows:

Suborder Suiformes
   Family Suidae   Pigs
         Tayassuidae   Peccaries
         Hippopotamidae Hippopotamuses
Suborder Tylopoda
   Family Camelidae   Camels and
                       llamas
Suborder Pecora
   Superfamily Traguloidea
   Family Tragulidae   Chevrotains
   Superfamily Cervoidea
   Family Moschidae   Musk-deer
         Cervidae   Deer
         Giraffidae   Giraffe and
                       okapis
   Superfamily Bovoidea
   Family Antilocapridae Pronghorns
         Bovidae   Cattle,   sheep,
                       goats and ante-
                       lopes

These groups differ in such features as the degree of digital reduction, the number of stomach compartments and the structure of the teeth. In the Suiformes the metapodials tend to be at least partially separate and the stomach has two to three chambers. The teeth are low-crowned. In the Tylopoda there are three stomach chambers, the metapodials are united, but the sole of the foot is formed by the middle as well as the distal phalanges, i.e. they are not unguligrade. In the Pecora, or true ruminants, there are four stomach chambers (although the third is reduced in the Traguloidea), the metapodials are fused, the cheek-teeth are high-crowned and ridged, and there are no upper incisors—instead the lower incisors bite against a hardened pad. Many of them bear paired horns or antlers on the head. The Bovidae are the largest, most successful family with 122 species. They are indeed the dominant herbivores of today and some species, like the bison in North America, the saiga in western and central Asia and the springbok of southwest Africa, existed in huge numbers, probably many millions,

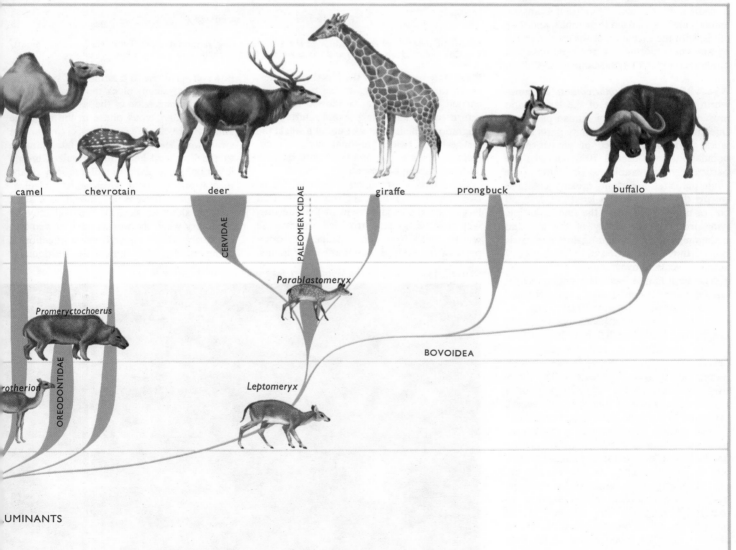

camel   chevrotain   deer   giraffe   prongbuck   buffalo

CERVIDAE

PALEOMERYCIDAE

Parablastomeryx

Promeryctochoerus

OREODONTIDAE

BOVOIDEA

Leptomeryx

...otherion

UMINANTS

Ascaris

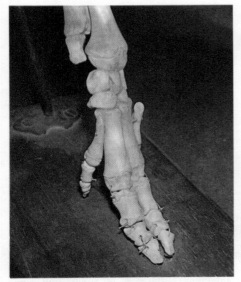

Foot bones of typical cloven-hoofed animal.

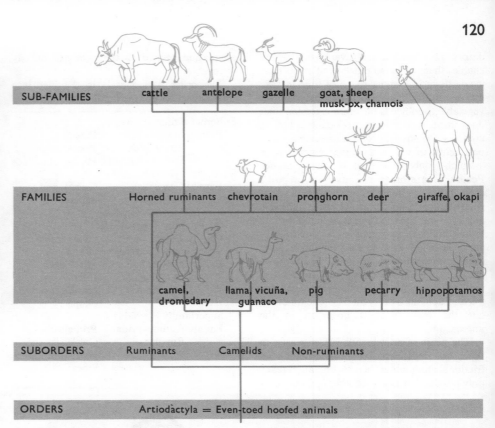

Schematic diagram of relationships of the Suiformes (pig, hippopotamus), Tylopoda (camels, lamas), the Cervoidea (deer, giraffe) and the Bovoidea (cattle, sheep and goats). See table on p. 119.

before their destruction by man. Even today, nearly 1 million Thomson's gazelles and ½ million gnu live on the Serengeti plain in Tanzania. Man's most important domestic animals are drawn from their ranks, and they alone, with the exception of the rodents, have paramount importance among mammals in human economy. CLASS: Mammalia. C.P.G.

ASCARIS *Ascaris lumbricoides,* a round-worm of man, it is one of the largest and most widely distributed of human parasites. Infections are common in many parts of the world and the incidence of parasitism in populations may exceed 70%; children are particularly vulnerable to infection. The adult parasites are stout, creamy coloured worms that may reach a length of 1 ft (30 cm) or more. They live in the small intestine, lying freely in the cavity of the gut and maintaining their position against peristalsis (the rhythmic contraction of the intestine) by active muscular movements.

The adult female has a tremendous repro-ductive capacity and it has been estimated that one individual can lay 200,000 eggs per day. These have thick, protective shells, do not develop until after they have been passed out of the intestine and for successful development of the infective larvae a warm, humid environment is necessary. The infec-tive larva can survive in moist soil for a considerable period of time (perhaps years), protected by the shell. Man becomes infected by accidentally swallowing such eggs, often with contaminated food or from unclean hands. The eggs hatch in the small intestine and the larvae undergo an involved and an, as yet unexplained, migration around the body before returning to the intestine to mature. After penetrating the wall of the intestine the larvae enter a blood vessel and are carried in the blood-stream to the liver and thence to the heart and lungs. In the

latter they break out of the blood capillaries, move through the lungs to the bronchi, are carried up the trachea, swallowed and thus return to the alimentary canal. During this migration, which may take about a week, the larvae moult twice. The final moult is com-pleted in the intestine and the worms become mature in about two months.

An infected person may harbour one or two adults only and, as the worms feed largely on the food present in the intestine, will not be greatly troubled, unless the worms move from the intestine into other parts of the body. Large numbers of adults,

however, give rise to a number of symptoms and may physically block the intestine. As in trichiniasis migration of the larvae round the body is a dangerous phase in the life-cycle and, where large numbers of eggs are swallowed, severe and possibly fatal damage to the liver and lungs may result. Chronic infection, particularly in children may retard mental and physical development. Medica-tion is often effective in removing the adult worms, although surgical removal may be necessary when the worms have moved into other organs. In regions where infection is common, hygienic measures, particularly

Cluster of ascidians, the red Gooseberry sea squirt *Dendrodoa grossularia.*

with regard to treatment and disposal of nightsoil, are essential in order to prevent reinfection.

Ascaris lumbricoides has probably evolved from the pig roundworm, *Asuum,* which is similar in many respects. Cross infection between man and pig is possible but to a limited extent only. FAMILY: Ascaridae, ORDER: Ascaridida, CLASS: Nematoda, PHYLUM: Aschelminthes.   D.W.

ASCIDIA, one of the largest genera of Sea squirts and the one which has given its name to the class Ascidiacea. Unlike the more primitive members of the class, *Ascidia* does not reproduce by budding but remains solitary throughout its life. The numerous species are all comparatively large, some up to 6 in (15 cm) long, and are found at all depths in the sea from the lower part of the sea-shore to the abyss and from the polar seas to the tropics. Some species are eaten, chiefly in Japan. FAMILY: Ascidiidae, ORDER: Enterogona, CLASS: Ascidiacea, SUB-PHYLUM: Urochordata, PHYLUM: Chordata.

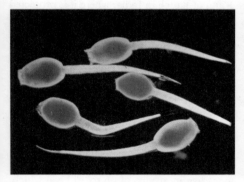

Tadpole larvae of ascidian *Dendrodoa grossularia.*

ASCIDIACEA, the largest class of the Sea squirts containing about 20,000 species. The vast majority are sessile (attached to rocks throughout adult life) and all are marine, hardly penetrating even into brackish water. They are locally abundant in relatively shallow waters, though they have been found in abyssal depths and also occur up to low water neaptide level. They sometimes occupy almost every inch of a rock surface or the bottom of a boat or dock. *Ciona* is a major fouling organism contributing greatly to reducing the speed of ships at sea. Caves near low water in the English Channel may be lined throughout by a coating of the cherry-sized red *Dendrodoa.*

Originally ascidians were budding animals, forming colonies by this means, but some species have become solitary. We can thus distinguish three grades of organization: colonial ascidians, in which the indi-

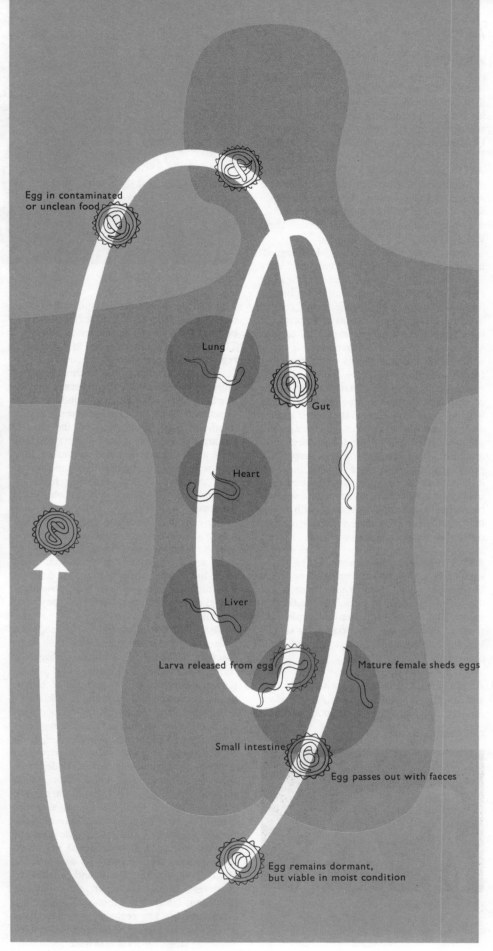

Life-cycle of *Ascaris lumbricoides* showing the stages passed through in man.

vidual 'zooids' are attached only at the base (e.g. *Clavelina*); solitary ascidians (e.g. *Ascidia, Ciona, Phallusia*); and compound ascidians in which the zooids are embedded in a common tunic or test, often sharing some organs (e.g. *Botryllus*). SUBPHYLUM: Urochordata, PHYLUM: Chordata.   D.B.C.

ASITYS, two species of a family long isolated in Madagascar. The family also includes two species of False sunbird *Neodrepanis* which were classified as true sunbirds (Nectariniidae) until anatomical studies linked them with the asitys.

Asitys are plump, rather long-legged, arboreal birds 5–6 in (13–15 cm) long. Very little is known about Schlegel's asity *Philepitta schlegeli* which inhabits the humid forests of western Madagascar and only a little more about the Velvet asity *P. castanea* which replaces it in the forests of eastern Madagascar. The male Velvet asity is black with yellow fringes to its feathers when freshly moulted, the male Schlegel's asity mainly yellowish with a black crown. Males of both species have a large greenish wattle, which surmounts the eye in the former species and surrounds it in the latter. The females and young of both species are duller and mainly greenish. The Velvet asity builds a suspended, pear-shaped nest of moss and fibres in which it lays three white eggs. Both species feed mainly on small fruits and are quiet solitary birds, but occasionally associate with flocks of other species. FAMILY: Philepittidae, ORDER: Passeriformes, CLASS: Aves.

ASP *Vipera aspis,* also known as the Aspic viper or June viper, of southern Europe, looks like the European adder or viper except that the tip of its snout is turned up, making a spike. The name has been misapplied to snakes elsewhere. See cobra. FAMILY: Viperidae, ORDER: Squamata, CLASS: Reptilia.

ASS, a horse-like animal but with longer ears and differing in colour and size. All wild asses *Equus asinus,* are very similar in appearance.

The African wild ass.

Jackasses (male asses) fighting.

The wild ass existed in three subspecies in the deserts and semi-deserts of northern Africa, but has been largely exterminated by man. Their range has been restricted to the Danakil region of Ethiopia where the total population numbers an estimated two to three hundred Nubian wild asses *E. a. africanus* and to northern Somalia, the Somali wild ass *E. a. somalicus.* There may also be some asses left in the Tibesti mountains of the central Sahara. It has not yet been ascertained that these asses are pure blooded wild asses; they may well have interbred with escaped domestic donkeys. A few breeding herds of African wild asses are kept in zoological gardens.

African wild asses are grey or reddish-brown and have a dark cross on their withers, one line running down the back, the other at right angles down to the shoulders. They often have dark, horizontal stripes on their legs, especially on the outer side, possibly a vestigial, zebra-like stripe-pattern. They have a shoulder height of 48 in (1·2 m).

The Asiatic wild asses are better known under the vernacular names of their subspecies: the onager *E. hemionus onager* of Iran, Afghanistan, Turkmenia and Rann of Kutch, western India; the kulan *E. h. hemionus* of Mongolia, and the kiang *E. h. kiang* of Tibet and the Himalayas. A further subspecies, the Syrian wild ass *E. h. hemippus* is now extinct. The onager, shoulder height 48 in (1·2 m), is light yellowish-brown in summer, but darker in winter. Its underparts, legs and muzzle are white. The kulan, shoulder height 50 in (1·35 m), is darker and more reddish-brown. The kiang, shoulder height 54 in (1·4 m), is the tallest of the Asiatic wild asses. Its coat is pale chestnut brown in summer and more reddish in winter.

Originally, the Asiatic wild asses had a range from Arabia, Syria and Turkey to northwest India and from the southern European USSR to Tibet and Mongolia. During the last few centuries they have been persecuted by man, being competitors of domestic stock for food and water, and their present range is now restricted to a few isolated areas. All subspecies can be considered to be in danger of extinction and of the onager alone there is a population of several hundred in a wildlife reserve, Badchys, in Turkmenistan, USSR. Another population of 8–900 head lives in the Little Rann of Kutch in India, where it is protected due to the vegetarian habits of the surrounding human population. Small numbers live in Iran and Afghanistan. The kulan is apparently limited to central Mongolia; no recent information is available on its numbers and status, and there are probably not more than a few hundred survivors of this race. The same is true for the kiang.

All wild asses are inhabitants of steppes, semi-deserts and even deserts, but they depend on surface water as they need to drink every two or three days. The Asiatic wild asses live in groups of up to 15 head which, during seasonal migrations, may join up to form larger herds. As in other equids, there is no set breeding time and foals are born in any month of summer.

Virtually nothing is known of the African wild ass's habits in the wild. Their social structure seems to resemble that of the Plains zebra. Little is known of the social structure of the Asian wild ass, but it is known that the groups consist of a stallion, a few mares, and their young, but these units do not seem to be permanent: mares have been observed to separate from their group when foaling. Normally, the stallion leads the group, but when they are attacked, the stallions keep to the rear and defend their mares and foals. During the rut the young males are chased from the group, by the stallion. FAMILY: Equidae, ORDER: Perissodactyla, CLASS: Mammalia.   H.K.

ASS. The ass of fable and proverb is portrayed as a stupid animal and its name has been transferred to an ignorant or silly person. Apparently this is due to the stupid expression and dull demeanour of the domesticated ass or donkey. Yet we also have the saying 'the wisdom of the ass' and from earliest times there are testimonies to its intelligence. Balaam's ass is well-known. The Romans held asses in high esteem: for riding, as they were hardier than horses, especially in desert country; as performers in circuses; and for medicinal purposes, asses' milk being more than a bath for Cleopatra, it was said to be very good for tuberculosis. The evidence for the ass's intelligence lies mainly in anecdotal form. One ass was ill-treated by a certain member of a party of travellers and 'would stand demurely whenever his old enemy was near, as if unconscious of his presence, until he was within reach of his heels, when a sharp kick, with a look of more than ordinary asinine stolidity, was the certain result.'

The ass has been a beast of burden especially in Asia and, as here, in North Africa.

ASSASSIN BUGS, or Kissing bugs, Blood-sucking conenoses or Masked hunters, predacious bugs usually living on the blood of other insects, but also attacking the higher animals and man. The 3,000 species are rather flattened, roughly oval-shaped insects, with small heads bearing protruding eyes and long antennae and with a prominent snout. The wings are folded flat on the back and the six long legs give the insect a superficial spider-like appearance. Many species found in human dwellings may be from $\frac{1}{2}$– $1\frac{1}{2}$ in (1·3–3·8 cm) long. The mouthparts, as with all members of Hemiptera, are tubular and adapted for piercing the host's body and sucking its blood. When the insect is not feeding, the mouthparts, which are termed collectively the rostrum, are carried out of sight underneath the head and body. The edges of the abdomen are flattened as thin plates visible at the sides of the closed wings and in some species the plates are brightly coloured with red, yellow or pink, although more generally the whole insect is brownish.

The majority of the Assassin bugs are found in the New World, especially Central America and northern South America. Other species occur in Europe, Africa (including Madagascar) and southern Asia.

Assassin bugs are active runners and good fliers. Most species live in the nests or burrows of rodents, armadillos and opossums. A few live in close association with man, spending the daytime in crevices in roofs and walls and feeding at night by sucking the blood of sleeping humans or domestic animals.

Several species of Assassin bugs (*Rhodnius* and *Triatoma*) are important as carriers and transmitters (vectors) of the frequently fatal Chagas' disease in Central and South America. Chagas' disease is caused by microscopic organisms called trypanosomes, similar to those transmitted by the Tsetse fly, which cause African sleeping sickness. Charles Darwin describes in his account of the voyage of the *Beagle* how he 'experienced an attack (for it deserves no less a name) of the benchuca, the great black bug of the Pampas'. It has been shown that this bug, *Triatoma infestans,* is very frequently infected with trypanosomes and Darwin's long history of ill health and eventual death in 1882 has been said to be the result of the bug attack in 1835. FAMILY: Reduviidae, ORDER: Hemiptera, CLASS: Insecta, PHYLUM: Arthropoda. M.J.P.

ASTACURA, one of the divisions of the decapod crustaceans, the tribe Astacura includes lobsters and crayfishes.

ASTROPOTHERIA, fossil mammal described under South American ungulates.

ATELOPODIDAE, a small family of frogs found in Central and South America. They are contained in the suborder Procoela and are most closely related to the toads (Bufonidae). They are distinguished from toads by the structure of their shoulder girdle; the two halves, instead of overlapping at the front as they do in toads, are fused down the midline, while another part of the shoulder girdle, the sternum, is missing.

There are only two genera, *Atelopus* and *Brachycephalus,* the former comprising about 25 species which are widespread in Central and South America while the single species of *Brachycephalus, B. ephippium,* is found in southern Brazil.

Externally also they are readily distinguished from toads, many of them having long bodies with very thin long legs. In some species the snout is beak-like while in others it is square, as though the tip had been cut off.

The Brown pelican of America, an example of Audubon's artistry.

It has a short, toad-like body with large bony knobs behind the eyes. It also has a large bony plate set in the skin of its back. This fits across the back like a saddle and is fused to the underlying vertebrae. Its function is uncertain but it is probably protective because this frog moves very slowly. Its skin is smooth except over the bony plate and is brilliant orange above and chrome yellow below. Its eyes, although not particularly large, are very conspicuous since they are completely black. The tadpoles of this species are similarly a bright orange colour but are very much larger than the adult.

The adults live on the forest floor under leaves and fallen tree trunks in the mountain forests of southern Brazil, coming out in large numbers in rainy weather. ORDER: Anura, CLASS: Amphibia. M.E.D.

AUDUBON J.J., 1785–1851. Haitian artist-naturalist, probably the most famous of all bird painters. Son of a French naval officer, he spent his boyhood in relative luxury in France where he developed an insatiable taste for natural history and a decided talent for drawing, birds figuring prominently in both activities. Sent to the USA when he was 18 he failed in business but with immense perseverence pursued his natural history interests and from 1820 concentrated, with his wife's support, on his monumental *Birds of America*. Published in four elephant folio volumes between 1827 and 1838, with 435 hand-coloured plates, the whole work cost about $100,000 to produce. Under 200 sets were issued at $1000 a set, and the few that remain are priceless. This, and the subsequent octave edition in seven volumes have had an enormous influence on the appreciation of natural history in general and ornithology in particular. Audubon was a pioneer in the naturalistic portraiture of birds and, although his treatment of his subjects has been criticized, his achievement is in no way exaggerated by the flourishing network of Audubon societies covering the United States.

AUKS, general term for members of the family Alcidae, chunky, marine diving birds with short wings used as flippers for swimming under water. There are 22 species of auks, if we include the garefowl, or Great auk, the large flightless species which became extinct in 1844. Two other species are commonly known as 'auks': the Razorbilled auk or razorbill *Alca torda* and the Little auk or dovekie *Plautus alle*. Other species are known as guillemots or murres (pronounced like the 'mur' in murmur) *Uria aalge,* murrelets, auklets, tystie (the Black guillemot) *Cepphus grylle* and puffins *Fratercula*

The pupil of the eye is horizontal and the ear disc is not visible. The skin may be either smooth or quite granular in texture.

The skin is poisonous and many species of *Atelopus* are brightly coloured. Zetek's frog *A. zeteki* from Panama is golden yellow with black spots and, perhaps because of its poison, is quite fearless, making no attempt to escape when approached. It is active during the day and its colour makes it very conspicuous. The Green mosaic frog *A. cruciger,* from Venezuela, on the other hand, it patterned with green and is well camouflaged as it sits on the mossy banks of streams.

A. stelzneri from Uruguay is black with orange hands and feet. When frightened it suddenly bends its head and legs backwards displaying its brightly coloured hands and feet. This warns its attacker of its poisonous nature. In this species the female, as well as the male is able to call. The eggs are laid in temporary rain pools and the tadpoles hatch out after only 24 hours.

The Gold frog *Brachycephalus ephippium* is a remarkable little frog. When fully grown it is only about ¾ in (20 mm) long, and only one of the fingers on each hand is well developed, the others being reduced to small lumps. Two of the toes on each foot are similarly reduced.

A colony of guillemots, or murres.

arctica. The family is an ancient one and is divided into 13 genera arranged in seven tribes.

Just as the penguins, which resemble the auks in many ways, belong to the southern seas so the auks, conversely, belong to the north. Their origin seems to have been in the area of the Bering Sea and their present distribution is in the North Pacific, North Atlantic and Arctic Oceans. The auks vary in length from 6½–30 in (16–76 cm). The plumage is largely black above and white beneath, though two of the Pacific species have a cryptically coloured breeding dress. The tail, legs and neck are short, which, with the short wings, stocky body and large head, gives the bird its chunky appearance. The Little auk, which has a stubby bill, is very reminiscent of a bumblebee when seen in flight from a distance. There is a considerable variation in the bill characters of the group. In the guillemots it is long and pointed; in the Great auks, razorbills and particularly in the puffins, it is deep and laterally compressed. As with other birds which spend much of their time in the water, the principal distinguishing features are on the head. In the puffins and some of the auklets the bill plates are highly coloured and sculptured. These plates are shed after the breeding season and replaced annually. Some species have ornamental plumes on the head and the lining of the mouth is generally brightly coloured. Some species also have brightly coloured feet.

Although rather feeble in flight, and taking wing with difficulty, auks are expert divers and underwater swimmers, using the wings in a half-open position to provide propulsion. The legs are placed well back on the body, for more efficient steering and the standing posture of auks is therefore rather upright. The Great auk in fact was very similar in appearance to a medium-sized penguin. The feet are seldom used for forward movement underwater, but function as steering vanes beneath the surface, and also in the air. They are of course webbed, although the hind toe—the first—is rudimentary or missing. The remaining three toes bear strong claws.

Auks eat many kinds of marine organisms, including worms, shellfishes (both mollusc and crustacean) and even algae, but the principal item in the diet of most species is fish. The prey is usually captured in deep water as, outside the breeding season, auks live out to sea. A certain amount of bottom-feeding also takes place, but this is more frequent when the adults are feeding chicks. The feeding specializations are illustrated by the different kinds of prey given to the young of Little auks, razorbills, guillemots and puffins. Up to three of these species may be fishing in the same waters at the same time, but excessive competition is avoided by preferences for different types of prey. The

Two common auks: the puffin (above) readily recognized by its coloured bill, and the razorbill

Little auk feeds its young on plankton and crustaceans, carried in cheek pouches; puffins concentrate on small fish fry and Sand eels; razorbills take fishes a little larger; and guillemots take the largest fishes of all. Thus a puffin may return to the nesting colony with as many as 30 small fishes held crosswise in its peculiar bill, while a razorbill carries fewer, larger fishes, in a longer bill. The guillemot, with the longest bill of all, carries the largest fishes—usually only one at a time—and the chick may swallow head first, a fish, longer than itself. When this happens the fish's tail remains hanging out of the chick's bill while the head end is digested. The bills of these three birds reflect the importance to them of concentrating on different types of prey. The effective fish-holding lengths of the bills of typical adult specimens are $1\frac{1}{2}$ in (3·6 cm) puffin; $1\frac{1}{8}$ in (4·1 cm) razorbill; and $2\frac{1}{4}$ in (5·7 cm) guillemot.

Auks are gregarious and usually breed in colonies. Some of these colonies are enormous and may consist of millions of birds. The sexes are externally very similar and both male and female share in the incubation of the egg or eggs and the feeding of the young. The nests, on rocky coasts or off-shore islands, are on ledges, fully exposed but usually inaccessible to climbers, or partially hidden in crevices or under boulders, or fully concealed in burrows. These burrows may be dug by the auks themselves or taken over from other animals, such as shearwaters or rabbits. A puffin has been seen to fly into a burrow which originally belonged to a rabbit and, after a short but sharp altercation, eject a shearwater.

The avoidance of direct competition between auks living in the same area is also shown in their choice of nest sites often on the same cliff. The Common guillemot, or murre, and Brünnich's guillemot, or Thick-billed murre *Uria lomvia,* lay their eggs on exposed ledges. The razorbill tends to lay in more sheltered positions on the ledges, sometimes quite out of sight; the Black guillemot, and the Little auk lay under cover of rocks; and the puffin nests in a burrow. The Black guillemot lays two eggs while all the other auks lay only one. In the Arctic auks' eggs, with those of other seabirds, have been harvested by man for centuries, and some of the seabird colonies of northern Russia are covered by conservation programmes because of this threat.

The time of the departure of auk fledglings from the nest varies considerably with the species. The young of Common and Brünnich's guillemots, for example, spend from 18–25 days on the bare cliff ledges before they go to sea. For the first few days after hatching the chick is rather helpless and in great danger of falling off its ledge and from exposure to the elements. From about the

sixth day chicks venture more frequently from beneath the parent, and soon begin to solicit food from any adult. The fledglings leave the nest and flutter down to sea before their primary wing feathers are fully developed and sea-going is therefore full of risks. Frequently the breeding ledges are hundreds of feet above the sea and the young birds may have to fly $\frac{1}{4}$ mile (0·4 km) or more in order to clear the rocks beneath. On this first flight they are usually accompanied by one or more adults. Sometimes the young try to take to the water before they are fully ready and in these circumstances they usually die of exposure or drown. The parents seem to actively try to prevent a premature departure by standing between the chicks and their destination.

The puffin chick is reared in the security of the nest burrow and can thus afford to take its time, developing fully before going to sea. It may take as long as 50 days to do this. The Pacific murrelets of the genera *Endomychura* and *Synthliboramphus,* however, are hatched in a highly advanced state and follow the adults to the water before they are two days old.

The nesting habits of the Marbled murrelet *Brachyramphus marmoratus,* the breeding range of which seems to be the coastal coniferous belt of the North Pacific region, are as yet unknown. Kittlitz' murrelet

B. brevirostris is highly unusual amongst auks in being a solitary nester, laying on bare ground amongst patches of snow above the tree-line in the mountains of Alaska, or on islands off the coast. Both species have cryptic breeding plumage, from which we may deduce that the Marbled murrelet is also a ground nester.

Vocalizations outside the breeding season are infrequent, but on or near the nesting sites they are quite varied, from the sibilant whistle of the Black guillemot to the harsh grunts, growls and moans of the razorbill and puffin. The calls mostly form part of the breeding displays, but aggressive notes are also used. The breeding displays also involve 'water dances' in a number of species, in which several birds swim around in lines and figures, or a pair of birds may perform mutual displays, with simple posturings and vocalizations and display of the coloured mouth lining. A considerable amount of billing also takes place, both on the water and at the breeding site.

The Bering Sea origin of the auks is suggested partly by the distribution of auks today. Some of them are circumpolar, but 16 species occur in the North Pacific, 12 of them nowhere else. In addition to the species already mentioned, the Pacific auks include the five auklets of the genera *Ptychoramphus* and *Aethia,* which are the ecological equival-

Two little auks, known in North America as dovekies.

ent of the Little auk in the North Atlantic and the Tufted and Horned puffins. The Tufted puffin *Lunda cirrhata* has the usual striking puffin bill plates, but it also has pendant tufts of feathers falling down behind on each side of the head. The Horned puffin, or Rhinoceros auklet, *Cerorhinca monocerata* has a peculiar short horn projecting upwards from the base of the upper mandible and a pair of white plumes running back on each side of the head, one from above the eye and the other from the corner of the mouth. Unlike other puffins it is nocturnal.

The auks form a highly successful group of seabirds. Some of the species number scores of millions of individuals. The hundreds or thousands of millions of auks in the oceans of the north play a significant role in the general ecological pattern and utilization of food materials in those regions. FAMILY: Alcidae, ORDER: Charadriiformes, CLASS: Aves.   P.M.D.

AUROCHS *Bos primigenius,* also called aurochsen or urus, the wild cattle of the Palearctic. The bulls were enormous, about 6 ft (2 m) high at the shoulder and with huge forward-curving horns. They were generally very dark brown, almost black, while the much smaller cows were reddish brown. The aurochs is the familiar large horned cattle seen in cave paintings such as those at Lascaux in France. It was the wild ancestor of the western domestic cattle and should strictly be referred to as a subspecies *Bos taurus primigenius* of the latter, rather than a full species. It may be impossible to decide whether bones of Neolithic age are of wild aurochsen or domestic stock. The wild forms were larger, had bigger horns and the back of the skull was relatively shorter, yet these features are, in any case, less marked in cow aurochsen and domestic stock would be mostly cows rather than bulls. Probably, the wild aurochsen were first hunted, later domesticated and then exterminated to prevent contamination of the domestic stock. Certainly, the last wild aurochs in Europe was killed in 1627, in Poland, and for a while, the German name aurochs was misapplied to the only other wild ox of Europe, the bison *Bos bonasus.*

In the 1930's two attempts were made to "recreate" aurochs by selective breeding from domestic cattle. In both attempts, by German zoos, various breeds were used such as Highland cattle and Camargue fighting cattle, which might retain primitive characteristics such as the large horns. The experiments seem to have been successful, for the original aurochs colouring and fierce temperament reappeared, and the recreated aurochsen now breed true. FAMILY: Bovidae, ORDER: Artiodactyla, CLASS: Mammalia.   D.W.Y.

White-backed magpie *Gymnorhina hypoleuca* from South and Central Australia and Tasmania.

AUSTRALIAN MAGPIES, a family (Cracticidae) of birds peculiar to Australasia, having mainly black, grey and white plumage and a generalized resemblance to crows or large shrikes. The name is sometimes restricted to species of the genus *Gymnorhina*. All have loud and often melodious calls. They occur in a wide variety of habitats wherever some trees are present, being tree-nesters. They make a typical cupshaped nest built mainly of sticks with a lining of finer material. The eggs have a brown, green or bluish ground colour, patterned with dark blotches or spots.

Species of the genus *Gymnorhina* are sometimes known as Piping crows or Bellmagpies, more often simply as magpies, and are the most crow-like in size, shape and movement, but have strikingly pied plumage, the head, wings and tail being black and normally most of the body being white. The pattern varies with locality and with age and from one to three different species are recognized. They feed mainly on the ground, walking about like crows, and take mainly insects but also any other small creatures that are available. Instead of nesting in pairs the birds usually belong to a larger social group which defends a communal territory against other similar groups. The individual females make their own nests within the territory, caring for the eggs and young, the males helping when the young fledge. They are generally aggressive birds. The groups indulge in loud melodious calling in chorus.

The four species of the genus *Cracticus*

are called butcherbirds (a name also used for the true shrikes, Laniidae). They are large-headed perching birds. The upper mandibles of their strong tapering bills have a sharp downward hook at the tip. The plumage is usually pied or grey, but one species is normally wholly black or shows a rufous phase, and rufous-brown is also present on the young of some other species. They take larger prey—reptiles, birds and mammals—than do other species of Australian magpies. They cannot use the feet for holding food and must wedge it in a fork or impale it on a thorn to dismember it. Unlike the other Australian magpies they normally keep in pairs and do not form sociable groups. They have loud musical calls and the clear, flutelike notes of the Pied butcherbird *C. nigrogularis* are exceptionally fine.

The final group, the currawongs of the genus *Strepera,* are variously regarded as two or six species, differing in voice or plumage. They resemble large, slenderly-built crows, and tend to have duller, brown or grey plumage with white wing-patches conspicuous during flight. Wings, tail and legs are relatively long, and the long tapering bill has a small hook at the tip. They feed on the usual range of small creatures, but whereas the other species only occasionally eat fruit the currawongs take greater quantities and may damage orchard crops. They have a greater variety of notes, including gong-like metallic and mewing calls. FAMILY: Cracticidae, ORDER: Passeriformes, CLASS: Aves.

AUSTRALIAN REGION, one of the six major zoogeographical regions. It includes Australia and the islands of its continental shelf, New Guinea and Tasmania.

Australia itself is centred on the Tropic of Capricorn and much of its interior is desert. The westerly trade winds provide a damper climate for the eastern edge of the continent and for Tasmania. These areas are therefore covered with grassland or, along the Eastern Highlands (almost the only mountains in Australia), some evergreen eucalyptus forest. The grasslands extend also through the northern part of the continent. Tropical rainforest covers New Guinea and the most extreme north of Australia.

Australia has been isolated from other land masses for longer than any other continent, since the Cretaceous Period, at the latest. Land vertebrates which evolved since that time have generally failed to colonize Australia. Although the early marsupials managed to enter the region, the early placental mammals did not. This is somewhat surprising, because the two groups probably evolved at much the same time. It may be that the route to Australia, even in the Cretaceous, lay along a chain of islands as it does today. If so, it is possible that the marsupials evolved slightly earlier than the placentals and succeeded in crossing before the gaps between the islands become so numerous or so wide that the placentals, appearing slighty later, found it impossible to follow. Alternatively, perhaps the route was an extremely difficult one for both groups and its successful passage by the marsupials was merely a fortunate chance which was denied to the placentals. However it may be, the marsupials found themselves in a continent completely empty of placentals, and were able to radiate into a great variety of unique forms. These Australian marsupials have paralleled many of the types of placental mammal. Cats, wolves, bears, mice, squirrels, jerboas, moles, anteaters, rabbits and badgers are all represented by marsupials which resemble them in both way of life and appearance, yet are wholly un related to them. In addition, the kangaroos and wallabies fill the role of the placental ungulates, though quite different from them in appearance.

Only two types of placental mammal reached Australia unaided: the bats and the rats. Bats had little difficulty in making the journey along the East Indies chain of islands. Rats are one of the most competent placentals in crossing sea barriers and a number of types have reached New Guinea, but only about half of these made the further crossing to Australia. Other placentals have been introduced by man: the Wild dog or dingo was probably brought in about 6,500 years ago, while cats and rabbits were introduced in the 19th century—the rabbits even-

tually becoming a serious pest in Australia until controlled by myxomatosis.

The long isolation of the Australian region is also the reason for the existence there, and nowhere else, of the very primitive mammals known as monotremes, including the duckbill or platypus (*Ornithorhynchus*) and the Spiny ant-eaters (*Tachyglossus* and *Zaglossus*). Another relict species is *Ceratodus*, the last survivor of a once world-wide type of lungfish, now found only in Queensland.

Only twelve of the 58 families of birds widespread in the Australian region are more or less exclusive to it, but nevertheless, these provide over 40% of all the species of Australian birds. The most important of these are the emus (of Australia only), cassowaries (mainly in New Guinea), honey-eaters, flower peckers. Birds of paradise (mainly in New Guinea) and bower birds. Australia also has many parrots, pigeons and Australian wrens.

The only other important group of vertebrates found solely in Australia are the Flapfooted lizards (family Pygopodidae). A recurrent evolutionary trend among lizards is the tendency to lose the limbs. The Flapfooted lizards are a prime example of this. Sometimes spoken of as snake-lizards, the twenty species are snake-like, lack fore-limbs entirely and have hindlegs that are no more than scaly flaps on the sides of the body, with no outward indication of joints or toes.

Because of the uniqueness of the Australian mammals, the marsupials, attention tends to be diverted from some of the other assets of the geological past relating to this continent and associated islands. There is, for example, a whole order of crustaceans, the Anaspidacea, which consists of six species. The first was discovered in the mountain streams of Tasmania, *Anaspides tasmaniae,* prawn-like and 3 in (7.5 cm) long, having a fully segmented body without a carapace, recalling ancestral crustaceans. They are, without doubt, survivors of an ancient group once more widely distributed and they bear a remarkable likeness to fossil remains found in the Carboniferous rocks, 300 million years old, in North America and Europe. Even so, Australia has no more than its fair share of archaic invertebrates.

Another of the invertebrate living fossils of Australia is peripatus, a caterpillar-like creature once regarded as a link between the ringed worms and the insects. Species of peripatus are also found in South Africa and South America and nowhere else in the world. This recalls the distribution of the remarkable living fossil, among fishes, the lungfish, with the only other living species in central Africa and South America.

It was this pattern of animal distribution that greatly helped to foster the idea of the paleozoic continent of *Gondwanaland lying mainly across the southern hemisphere.

It is these connections between the fauna of Australia and the faunas in other parts of the world and especially of the southern hemisphere that help to build a picture of past events, when Australia was joined to the rest of the land masses. See Continental drift.
C.B.C.

AUSTRALIAN TREECREEPERS, six species of finch-sized, slender-billed, strong-footed birds which are unrelated to other treecreepers but resemble them in taking insects from crevices while spirally ascending vertical tree-trunks or branches. However, they also feed on the ground. When climbing their tails are not pressed to the tree but held away from it and they perch crossways on twigs like normal perching birds. The plumage is grey or brown with streaked areas and light buff patches are visible on spread wings in flight. The nest is a cup built in a hole or hollow branch and the eggs are heavily spotted. FAMILY: Climacteridae, ORDER: Passeriformes, CLASS: Aves.

AUSTRALIAN WRENS, a subfamily of small, slender-billed insectivorous birds usually regarded as warblers although some may be related to babblers. Their habitats range from forests to deserts with sparse vegetation. They build domed nests. The best known, the Blue wrens *Malurus* spp, have vividly-coloured males, and additional birds assist nesting pairs. FAMILY: Muscicapidae, ORDER: Passeriformes, CLASS: Aves.

AUSTRALOPITHECINES, literally 'southern apes', a group of extinct ape-like men, with small brains and fairly upright stance. See man, evolution of. FAMILY: Hominidae, ORDER: Primates, CLASS: Mammalia.

AUTECOLOGY AND SYNECOLOGY, the former is the study of a population of one particular organism in relation to its environmental conditions while the latter refers to the study of the relationships between groups of different species and their environment. In the case of autecological studies emphasis is usually laid on the life-history and behaviour of the organism as a means of adaptation to the environment. Synecological studies concentrate not only on the physical environment, but also try to discover and explain the interactions between the different species of the community. The line between autecology and synecology is not in fact hard and fast (synecological studies often include much autecological information) and the terms are not now so widely used as in the past. In their place the concept of 'level of organization' has grown up. In this system the different areas of ecology are related to the level of biological organization being studied. The most commonly used are individual, population, community and *ecosystem

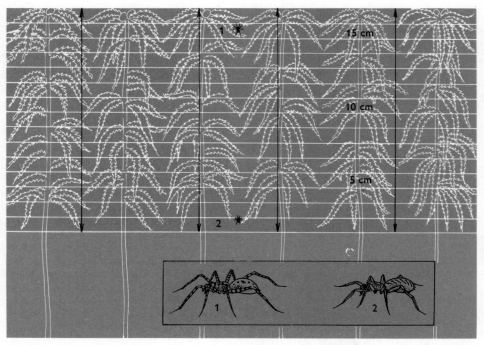

Two species of spiders (l. *Pirata piraticus*, 2. *Lycosa pullata*) provide an example of autecology, one species living on the heads of sphagnum moss, the other on the water surface beneath.

ecology. The first two divisions correspond to the term autecology while synecology includes both the study of communities as such and also the interdependent complex of a community and its characteristic physical environment which the term ecosystem describes. The difference between the two aspects of ecology is perhaps best illustrated by examples which outline the methods used.

An interesting autecological study on two species of Wolf spider, *Lycosa pullata* and *Pirata piraticus,* will illustrate the point. Both species occur in sphagnum bogs in Denmark which are water-logged throughout the year. The individual stems of the sphagnum moss grow to about 4 in (10 cm) above the water surface where they produce a canopy of bushy growth. This results in two horizontal surfaces, that of the water itself and that of the sphagnum heads.

The distribution of the two species was examined in the field and their temperature and humidity preferences studied in the laboratory. Although the two spiders were always found together on the same bogs, they rarely came into contact since one, *Lycosa pullata,* lived on the surface of the sphagnum heads while the other, *Pirata piraticus,* lived on the water surface. The first species had a temperature preference of about 86°F (30°C) in the laboratory and chose humidities well below saturation. *Pirata,* on the other hand, preferred temperatures of about 68–72°F (20–22°C) and a saturated atmosphere. The temperature at which heat stupor set in (i.e. at which the animal dies if left for more than a very short period) was also measured. It was found to

be about 95°F (35°C) in the case of *Pirata* and 109°F (43°C) in that of *Lycosa.* Measurements of the microclimate made on the surface of the sphagnum heads and of the water respectively showed that the preferences of the two spiders corresponded very closely to the temperatures and humidities found in their habits. A further interesting observation showed that when the females of *Pirata* were carrying egg-cocoons on their abdomens their whole behaviour pattern changed. During this period they would climb to the top of the sphagnum stems and thrust the abdomen plus the attached cocoon into the warmer air above. Apparently the optimum temperature for the development of the eggs is well above that for the adult spider and during the incubation period the temperature preference shifted from 68–72°F (20–22°C) to 79–86°F (26–30°C), only a few degrees below the thermal death point of the adult.

As a contrast to this approach to ecological problems, a study of decomposition of acorns provides an example of a synecological study. The process of decomposition is affected by the structure of the acorn itself which consists basically of three parts. Protecting the nut is the sclerotic layer, the hard woody shell around the outside. Inside this are the parenchyma and fibre layers which are not as hard as the sclerotic layer, but also have a protective function. Finally the 'nut' proper is in fact the living embryo which has a high fat content and is the most important source of food for organisms living in the acorn. The decay of acorns can be divided into five stages based on the successive de-

struction of the various regions outlined above. The stages are: 1 any stage in the initial attack on the nut which does not prevent development of the embryo; 2 the destruction of the embryo by, for example, an insect grub; 3 the decay of the parenchyma and fibrous layers and the reduction of the mass of faeces and dead embryo tissue left from stage two; 4 the decay of the woody shell and the 'cup'; and 5 the so-called 'mounding' stage when the shell has lost its identity and is being incorporated into the soil.

Stage one and part of stage two usually occur while the acorn is still on the tree. The most important initial colonizers are a weevil *Curculio rectus* and a moth *Melissopus latiferreanus.* The former lays an egg in the nut and the emerging larva burrows through the embryo, consuming roughly half of it as it does so. The moth lays its eggs on the outside of the nut and the larva bites its way through the shell and again eats the embryo. In this case each larva needs two to three nuts to complete its development.

Stage two is usually brought about by the initial colonizers plus another moth *Valentinia glanduella.* The larva of this species feeds on the remainder of the embryo and the faeces of the initial invaders, reducing them to dry fibrous pellets. Also during this stage larvae of two species of Gall midge enter the nut. The importance of these is probably that they carry spores of fungi (chiefly a species of *Penicillium* and one of *Fusarium*) which initiate decay in the embryo.

During stage three the parenchyma and fibrous layers of the outer wall undergo decay. This is brought about largely by the fungi mentioned above, when the Gall midge larvae leave the embryo and enter the parenchyma layer. However, as this layer begins to soften, two species of springtail *Tullbergia* and *Xenylla,* enter it in large numbers. These feed on both the fungi and cellular material and thus contribute to decomposition of the parenchyma.

By stage four the nut consists of a hollow shell. The breakdown of this shell is brought about by one of two species of fungi. The Honey fungus (*Armillaria mellea*) is capable of breaking down woody tissue and results in 'rapid' decomposition. The shells attacked by this species were completely decomposed in about one year. The other species of fungus (*Chaetomium elatum*) can only decompose cellulose, and the decomposition of the shell by this species takes place extremely slowly. During this stage of decomposition many animals characteristic of the forest floor in general will take refuge in the shell. Finally in stage five the weakened shell gradually collapses and becomes incorporated in the humus of the forest floor.

A comparison of the two types of ap-

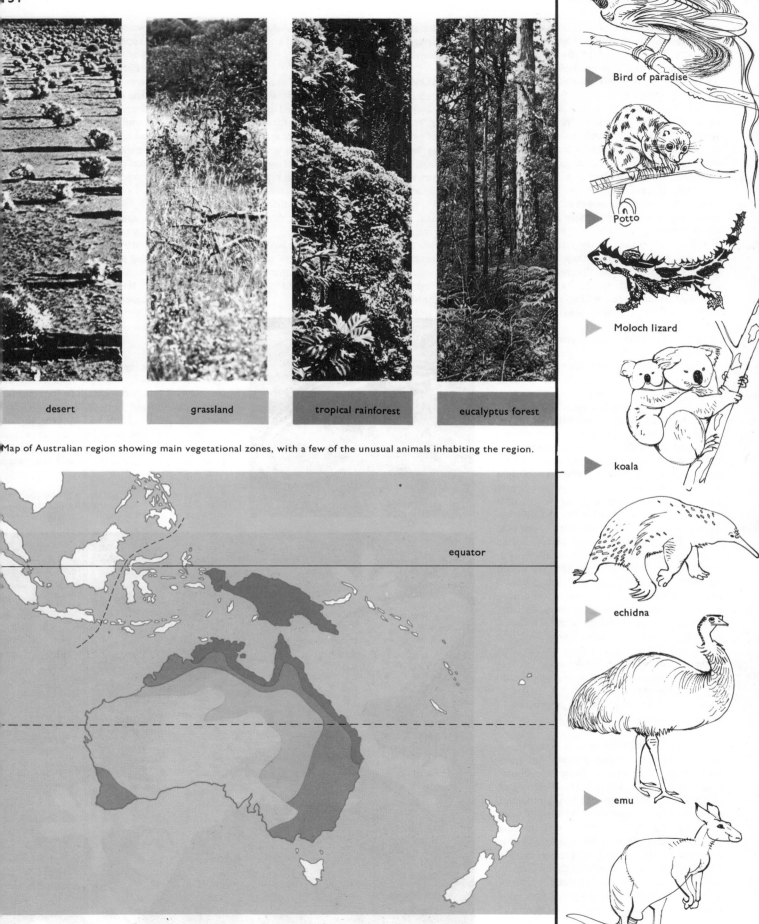

desert

grassland

tropical rainforest

eucalyptus forest

Map of Australian region showing main vegetational zones, with a few of the unusual animals inhabiting the region.

equator

Bird of paradise

Potto

Moloch lizard

koala

echidna

emu

kangaroo

proach to ecological problems can now be made and their advantages and disadvantages can be mentioned briefly. Clearly the importance of the first example is that the distribution of the two spiders can be explained in terms of physical factors of the environment. It also shows that the behaviour of the animal is not fixed but changes in a way that tends to maximize the chances of survival of the species as a whole. Attention is thus focused on the basic biology of the two spiders as a factor affecting their 'fitness' to the environment. It should be mentioned, however, that even in this clearly autecological study a synecological framework is found, since the spiders' distribution is related to the structure of the plant community in which they live. Furthermore, such studies on the preferences of animals provide only the limits to their possible performance, and within a suitable environment their population size is likely to be determined by other factors.

Such factors form an important part of synecological studies. It is clear from the second example that the decomposition of acorns, far from being a chance process, follows a clearly defined series of stages, each of which is brought about by a more-or-less constant group of animals and micro-organisms. The relationships in time between the different members of this community and the way in which various possible food resources are partitioned between different animals and micro-organisms is clearly shown. Each successive group of animals modifies the environment within the acorn in such a way as to permit the entry of the next group. Emphasis is therefore placed not so much on the effect of the physical environment on the animals as on the interaction between different animals and their effect on the environment itself. Clearly both autecological and synecological methods have advantages and disadvantages. The one, autecology, tends to be intensive while the other, synecology, is extensive (in the strict sense of the terms). While both provide useful contributions to ecology, each should be complemented by the other if we are to obtain a clear view of the workings of natural systems.   A.R.S.

AUTOHAEMORRHAGE. A number of snakes 'play dead' when attacked but autohaemorrhage is an even stranger behavioural response to attack found in the West Indian wood-snakes. When attacked by a predator, or manhandled in any way, these small boas first coil and then secrete an evil smelling substance from their anal glands. This is followed by the gorging of their eyes with blood which makes them cinder-red, and an actual release of blood from palatal capillaries which oozes between the jaws. It is presumed that the combination of offensive odour and blood letting deters the attacker. Autohaemorrhage is also seen in the lizard known as the Horned toad.

AUTOTOMY, the ability of lizards and the tuatara, among reptiles, to shed the posterior region of the tail when this is seized by a predator. There is a cleavage plane across the middle of one, or all, of the tail vertebrae, the two bony halves of the vertebra being joined in cartilage. This septum, or plane of weakness, gives when stressed and the tail region behind it separates. Lizards can regenerate the lost region of the tail. This defence mechanism is absent in the snakes despite their derivation from lizards.

The word is also used for higher arthropods, notably crustaceans, that throw off a leg that is injured or seized by a predator and is later regrown. Some worms can throw off part of the body and then replace it.

AVADAVAT, two species of Asian weaverfinch frequently kept in captivity by aviculturists. The term is usually restricted to the Red avadavat *Estrilda amandava,* also known as the Tiger finch, Strawberry finch or Red waxbill. The avadavat is small, about the size of the wren, and differs from other members of its family in having both breeding and non-breeding plumages. In the breeding season the male is basically a bright coppery or crimson red. FAMILY: Estrildidae, ORDER: Passeriformes, CLASS: Aves.

AVICULTURE, the keeping of birds in captivity for study or pleasure. The birds are usually kept in large cages or aviaries and attempts are often made to induce them to breed by providing correct food and a suitable environment. There are many flourishing avicultural societies throughout the world. In some cases the keeping and breeding of birds in captivity has resulted in rare species being saved from extinction. See Hawaiian goose.

AVOCETS, wading birds of the genus *Recurvirostra,* which, with the stilts, make up the family Recurvirostridae. The four species are characterized by a long, slender, markedly upcurved bill and by long legs in proportion to body size; the legs trail behind the tail in flight. Their plumage is chiefly black and white (with the exceptions noted

A skink (left) with its tail and a gecko (below) after using the familiar lizard trick of autotomy, throwing off part of the tail.

Avocet, handsome wading bird with a turned-up bill, the victim of marsh drainage.

below), though immature birds retain some brown feathers. The sexes are similar.

The avocet *R. avosetta* breeds in the Palearctic and Ethiopian faunal regions, chiefly on the coasts of the North Sea, the southern Baltic and around the Mediterranean, but also inland, in the Balkans and from the Black Sea south to Iraq and east to Mongolia. A few breed also in South Africa. Thus the temperatures tolerated by this species at its breeding grounds vary from about 60–90°F (15–32°C). The Palearctic populations winter chiefly in Africa, mainly on the salt and alkaline lakes of the East African Rift Valley, and in southeast Asia. Those wintering in South Africa may only be local birds. In recent years some have wintered on estuaries in the southwest of the British Isles.

In other parts of the world, the avocet is replaced by other members of the genus; indeed, some taxonomists believe the other three species to be but geographical races of one and the same species. In Australia, the genus is represented by the Red-necked avocet *R. novaehollandiae,* which rarely moves outside that country. On the American continent there is one migrant and one resident form. The somewhat larger American avocet *R. americana* breeds as far north as southern Canada but winters in Central America, while in the salty lagoons of the high Andes is found the Chilean avocet *R. andina.* The basic plumage colour-pattern of these three species is similar to that of the avocet, except that the American and Red-necked avocets have some reddish-brown on the head and neck.

Avocets nest colonially on muddy or sandy islands, sometimes covered with vegetation. They use little or no nest material on the sandy sites, but make a lining of dead plants on muddy surfaces. They lay a single clutch of usually four eggs, though replacement clutches are often laid if the first clutch or young nestlings are lost. (Replacement layings are rare in waders breeding in the Arctic, where the season favourable for rearing broods is much shorter than in the temperate or Mediterranean zones.)

Avocets frequent shallow lakes, marshes or mudflats at all times of year, with a preference for saline or brackish conditions, particularly in the breeding season. They feed on small crustaceans, by sweeping the slightly open bill from side to side, sifting the first few inches of water, or the liquid top surface of muddy deposits. Sometimes they take insects from the surface, but usually they wade deep into the water, which may reach well above their intertarsal (knee) joint.

With their striking plumages, avocets' displays are chiefly visual, though they are by no means silent birds. Displays involve not only pairs but also groups; wings are used more than bills in fighting. FAMILY: Recurvirostridae, ORDER: Charadriiformes, CLASS: Aves.   P.R.E.

AVOIDANCE BEHAVIOUR comprises escape responses evoked by various stimuli which act as token indications of possible harm to animals. Typical of these are moving shadows. The scallop *Pecten,* for example, responds to dark stripes moved in front of it in different ways according to the speed of movement; the stimuli are detected by the row of eyes on the edge of its mantle. When the stripes are moved at speeds between 11·6 and 24·6 cm per sec, the mantle edge is withdrawn and the shells are closed; at slower speeds, between 4·96 and 7·7 cm per sec, the shell is not completely closed and the tentacles fringing the mantle are left out. These tentacles are sensitive to chemicals and can detect the presence of substances given out into the water from a starfish, the

scallop's main enemy. The shell also remains fully open with tentacles out in response to stripes moving at slower speeds down to about 1·7 mm per sec but below this speed the animal ceases to respond. Thus the scallop's visual responses are adapted to picking up the first indications of a fast moving predator, such as an octopus, and also those of a slow moving predator, the starfish, the presence of which is then confirmed chemically by the tentacles, after which the scallop snaps its shell shut.

A number of herbivorous Sea snails are preyed upon by other Sea snails. Thus a Top shell *Melagraphia aethiops* when touched by the whelk *Lepsia haustrum* raises its shell and swings it violently through 180° several times before crawling away. This may have the effect of throwing off the predator. The Pond snail *Physa fontinalis* behaves in a similar way when it is touched by the leech *Glossiphonia complanata* which preys upon it. These responses seem to be made to chemical stimuli from the predator. Very possibly the behaviour described so far is inborn but it is possible for avoidance behaviour to be acquired, especially by the higher animals. Thus, once a young bird has taken a noxious insect into its mouth it will not attempt to eat the same kind of insect on another occasion. Since insects of this kind often have warning colouration, the bird quickly learns to associate the striking appearance with the unpalatable taste. Cinnabar moth caterpillars, for example, have unpleasant irritant hairs and their bodies are marked with black and yellow rings. Often the learned response is generalized to other similarly coloured insects, hence the value to the harmless hoverflies of their black and yellow colouring which makes them look so much like wasps.

Animals can be taught to avoid unpleasant punishing stimuli when these are signalled by some other harmless stimulus. A rat standing on a metal grid, in a laboratory experiment, moves off it when a light flashes, after it has been taught that a shock will follow through the grid in 5 sec. Moreover, it will continue to do this indefinitely. This poses a problem for those holding the view of learning which insists that reinforcement is essential. The rat always leaves the grid as soon as the light flashes and before receiving the reinforcing punishment stimulus, showing that it now has an understanding of the consequences of the flash of light. The scallop, on the other hand, reacts automatically whatever the source of the moving shadow.   J.D.C.

AXIS DEER, alternative name for the chital or Indian spotted deer *Axis axis,* a common deer of India and Ceylon, reddish-brown with white spots. For further details see Deer.

AXOLOTL *Ambystoma mexicanum,* neotenous larva of the Mole salamander, is confined to certain lakes around Mexico city. It measures 4–7 in (10–17·5 cm) in length and is usually black or dark brown with black spots, but white or pale pink albino forms are common. The legs and feet are relatively small and weak while the tail is long. A fin runs from the back of the head along the animal's back to the tail and then under the tail. Breathing is by three feathery gills on either side just behind the head and immediately in front of the forelimbs. During mating the male attracts the female by an elaborate courtship display as he secretes certain chemicals from abdominal glands and makes violent movements of the tail, thought to serve in dispersing the chemicals. Sperm is deposited in a packet or spermatophore which the female picks up from the bottom with her cloaca. Fertilization is therefore internal. The female lays 200–600 eggs in April-May and the young hatch 2–3 weeks later, reaching their maximum length by the winter when they hibernate. They eventually become sexually mature and are able to breed while still in a larval condition. That is, they are neotenous. The axolotl was assigned to a separate genus *Siredon* until it was discovered that under certain conditions it could lose its external gills and larval characteristics and metamorphose into an adult salamander. The neoteny of the axolotl seems to be due to a deficiency of iodine in the water.

In fact the word 'axolotl' is Mexican for 'water sport' and the animal is eaten as a delicacy.

In some instances the term axolotl may be used in a more general way for the neotenous larvae of other salamanders. For example, the larvae of the Tiger salamander *Ambystoma tigrinum,* which develop in cold water at high altitudes, fail to metamorphose and are often

The axolotl can be made to turn into a typical salamander.

This is what the axolotl looks like when made to 'grow up'.

referred to as the 'axolotl' of the Rocky Mountains.

The axolotl keeps well in captivity but must have moving prey and will ignore still dead food. Axolotls cannot usually be kept together however, since they are liable to bite off each other's gills, pieces of tail or feet. FAMILY: Ambystomatidae, ORDER: Candata, CLASS: Amphibia.   R.L.

AYE-AYE *Daubentonia madagascariensis,* a nocturnal mammal, about the size of a cat, with coarse black hair, large membranous ears, big forward-directed eyes and a bushy tail. The head and body length is 16 in (40 cm) and the tail is 22 in (55 cm). This is perhaps the most peculiar member of the order Primates. Its appearance and nocturnal habits make it eerie enough, and the presence of an elongated third finger on each hand adds a bizarre touch. It is therefore not surprising that villagers in Madagascar regard this animal as an evil omen. If one is

found near a village, it is either killed, or the village is abandoned.

Despite its peculiarities, the aye-aye is almost certainly a member of the lemur group (see Prosimii), and it is restricted to Madagascar like all other lemurs. It is a rain-forest form, and its natural distribution range is the northeastern coastal forest. However, destruction of the forest habitat of the aye-aye has led to the virtual extinction of this remarkable species. Recently, a dozen aye-ayes have been introduced on the island reserve of Nosy Mangabe in the Bay of Antongil (northeast Madagascar), and this may well be the only chance of preserving the species. The introduced animals appear to have settled down well, and they may breed to give a viable colony.

Ayes-ayes typically occur high up on the vertical trunks and larger branches of trees in the rain-forest. They have a mixed diet of insect and plant food, but most of their energy is spent in hunting insects. Here, the two main peculiarities of the aye-aye are brought into play. Unlike other lemurs, *Daubentonia* has two continuously-growing incisors in both upper and lower jaws. The canines are missing, and there is a gap (diastema) between the incisors and the premolars. This typical gnawing type of dentition is combined with the long, thin middle finger of each hand in the search for wood-boring insect larvae. The aye-aye seems to use both its sense of smell and its large, mobile ears to locate the larvae beneath the bark of dead branches. The incisor teeth are then used in a rapid, intense fashion to make a hole, and the thin middle finger of one hand is used to hook out the larva. An early report suggested that the aye-aye uses its elongated finger to tap on the bark when searching for larvae, but this is probably untrue. Most of the animal's nocturnal activity is taken up with finding and eating larvae. In the remaining periods, small quantities of fruit are eaten. Once again, the incisors are used to break the skin or shell of the fruit, and the middle finger is used to hook out tasty morsels. The small pieces of fruit are passed into the mouth with the finger, between the incisors and the premolars. The aye-aye can also combine its two types of food by searching for parasitic larvae in the kernels of soft fruit.

Aye-ayes build complicated nests in bowl-like forks of trees, about 40 ft (12 m) up, and consisting of a framework of thin branches interwoven with leaves. Within a given home-range, several nests are found, and it is likely that the aye-aye moves from one to the other for varying periods. Relatively old nests are repaired and strengthened from time to time, and a nest may eventually be abandoned altogether. This is a solitary species. Each individual has a fairly large home range with its own group of nests, and cries may be exchanged between adjacent range-owners. Occasionally, fights between neighbours occur.

Very little is known about reproduction in this animal, because of its rarity. It has seldom been observed under natural conditions, and even purely skeletal information is very rare. Like most lemurs, the aye-aye has one offspring at each birth, and it seems that this is carried around on the mother's back in the manner typical for the larger lemurs. The female has only two teats (mammae), and the stage of development of the young at birth indicates that the gestation period is quite long, probably being about five months, as with other larger lemurs such as the Ring-tailed lemur. The infant remains with the mother for some time, sharing the nest with her during the day, and probably learning a lot from her behaviour before becoming independent.

The most fascinating question regarding the aye-aye concerns its relationship to other mammals. When the first specimen was found, its squirrel-like appearance led early authors to place it in the order Rodentia. This interpretation was strengthened by the observation that the aye-aye has continuously-growing incisors and that there are claws rather than nails on most of the digits. In fact, *Daubentonia* was originally entitled *Cheiromys* (signifying a rodent with grasping extremities) and was for a long time referred to by this name. It was only when its anatomy was studied in detail that the conclusion was reached that it is actually a very unusual lemur. As with all members of the Prosimii, the big toe is opposable, and there is a 'toilet-claw' on the second toe of the hindfoot. In the skull, there is a bony arch (post-orbital bar) behind the eye, and the fine details of skull structure show typical Primate features. Finally, the placentation is remarkably like that of all other Madagascar lemurs and leaves no doubt that *Daubentonia* is an aberrant and very specialized lemur.

The only other member of the family Daubentoniidae is a relatively recent fossil aye-aye, *Daubentonia robustus,* which was larger than the living form but resembled it in all other characters of the skeleton. Most authors derive all lemurs from a common ancestor isolated on Madagascar about 50 million years ago, but some of the peculiar features of *Daubentonia* suggest that it has been distinct for longer than this and was derived from a separate ancestral form isolated on Madagascar when the island was first formed. FAMILY: Daubentoniidae, SUB-ORDER: Lemuriformes, ORDER: Primates, CLASS: Mammalia.   R.D.M.

AYSHEAIA *Aysheaia pedunculata,* a fossil onychophoran known only from the Middle

The aye-aye is nocturnal and therefore difficult to photograph in its natural surroundings. The author succeeded after much patience in photographing one in Madagascar, while it was eating fruit.

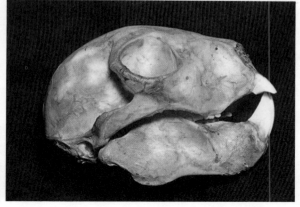

.Skull of an aye-aye showing the rodent-like, continuously growing incisors.

Cambrian Burgess Shales of western Canada. It was a soft-bodied animal related to the living genus *Peripatus,* which it seems to have resembled in most respects, but had branched antennae and only ten body segments compared with the unbranched antennae and 15–43 body segments of the living forms. CLASS: Onychophora, PHYLUM: Arthropoda.

AYU, the common name for *Plecoglossus altivelis,* a peculiar salmon-like fish found in Japan. Most of the salmonid fishes have pointed teeth but the ayu, amongst other anatomical peculiarities, has plate-like teeth. Because of this, it is placed in a family of its own, the Plecoglossidae.

The ayu, which grows to about 12 in (30 cm), migrates into freshwater to spawn. During the upstream migration, Japanese fishermen used to bring their trained cormorants at night to the rivers, attach rings round the throats of the birds and then release them into the water. The ring prevents the cormorant from completely swallowing the ayu and on the return of the bird the fisherman takes the fish from the cormorant and sends it off on another foray. In this way up to 50 ayu can be caught by one cormorant in a night. Cormorant fishing is being replaced by other methods and is now little more than a tourist spectacle. FAMILY: Plecoglossidae, ORDER: Salmoniformes, CLASS: Pisces.

BABBLERS, previously included in a separate family, the Timaliidae, are now considered to be a subfamily, the Timaliinae, within the enormous family Muscicapidae, which includes the thrushes and warblers. The parrotbills have often been included with the babblers in the Timaliinae. The 250 species of babblers include a great diversity of groups of birds which are only doubtfully more closely related to each other than to other groups.

The babblers can be divided conveniently into a number of tribes (the name of a tribe ends in—ni). These include the jungle-babblers (Pellorneini), scimitar-babblers and wren-babblers (Pomatorhini), tit-babblers and tree-babblers (Timaliini), song-babblers (Turdoidini), rockfowl (Picathartini) and ground-babblers (Cinclosomatini). Both the rockfowl and ground-babblers have often been included in separate subfamilies, respectively the Picathartinae and Cinclosomatinae, while the rockfowl have also been considered to be a separate family, the Picathartidae, related to crows and starlings. In addition, the wren-tit *Chamaea fasciata* of the Pacific coast of North America is nowadays thought to be a close relative of the babblers. However, its affinities are disputed and it is often included in a family of its own, the Chamaeidae. The effect of including it among the babblers would be to extend the range of the latter to the New World, for otherwise the babblers are entirely an Old World group.

The birds included in this assemblage have comparatively few characteristics in common. However, most babblers are noisy (hence their name), but otherwise inconspicuous, inhabitants of forest and thick scrub and the majority occur in flocks, often within the mixed species flocks that are so characteristic of tropical forests. For the most part babblers are insectivorous, though a number of species, particularly among the song-babblers, supplement their diet with fruit outside the breeding season.

The jungle-babblers are rather nondescript brownish species which can be divided into two distinct ecological groups. For example, species of *Pellorneum* and *Trichastoma* are mainly terrestrial and have short wings and tails but long legs and strong feet. On the other hand, species of *Malacopteron* are more arboreal, and consequently have longer wings and tails but shorter legs. Jungle-babblers occur in both the Ethiopian and Oriental regions, extending as far eastwards as the Philippines and Celebes.

Scimitar-babblers and wren-babblers, though closely related, differ considerably in appearance. Typical scimitar-babblers, such as species of *Pomatorhinus,* have long curved bills, long tails and short legs, while typical wren-babblers, such as species of *Ptilocichla* and *Napothera,* have short straight bills, short tails and long legs. Scimitar-babblers forage acrobatically around branches and creepers, probing with their long bills and using their long tails as a balance. By contrast, wren-babblers are terrestrial, as their long legs and short tail would suggest.

A babbler, the White-necked rockfowl *Picathartes oreas.*

These two groups are connected by species, in genera such as *Pomatostomus* and *Rimator,* which are intermediate in both their proportions and their ecology. Scimitar-babblers and wren-babblers occur from the Himalayas to Australia.

The tit-babblers and tree-babblers, as exemplified by the genera *Macronus* and *Stachyris,* are more uniform in size and proportions than the previous groups. As their names suggest, they are mainly arboreal and they forage in an acrobatic tit-like manner. They occur mainly in the Oriental region, where they range from India to the Philippines, Borneo and Java, though four species of *Neomixis* are confined to Madagascar.

The song-babblers are by far the largest and most diverse of the babbler tribes, and consist of about 140 species divided among 17 genera. They range in size from about 4–12 in (10–30 cm). Species of *Turdoides* are characteristic of the Middle East and the drier areas of the Ethiopian and Oriental regions, where they occur in almost any kind of thick scrub. Most other species occur in forest, by far the majority of them in the Oriental region. They include the laughing-thrushes *Garrulax,* most of which are large and noisy, while many are beautifully patterned. A few sing particularly well and are much prized as cage-birds in China. Species of *Pteruthius, Myzornis* and *Leiothrix* are also prettily marked and one of the latter, the Red-billed leiothrix *L. lutea,* is a very popular cage-bird more commonly known as the Pekin robin.

The rockfowl were formerly thought to be related to starlings (Sturnidae) but are currently thought to be large and specialized babblers. The two species have heads completely devoid of feathers, hence their alternative name of Bald crows. In one species, the Grey-necked rockfowl *Picathartes gymnocephalus,* the bald head is bright yellow; in the other, the White-necked rockfowl *P. oreas,* it is pink. Both species have short rounded

Yellow-eyed babbler *Chrysomma sinense* of southeast Asia in its nest of grass bound with cobwebs.

Stachyris striata, one of the tit-babblers at its nest among reeds.

wings, a long tail and long legs and are said to move gracefully on the ground by means of enormous hops. They live in the forests of West Africa, but only in areas in which large moss-covered boulders, cliffs and caves abound.

The ground-babblers are another particularly diverse group, as is emphasized by the range of vernacular names that are given to various genera. Thus the group includes among its 20 or so species the rail-babblers *Eupetes* and quail-thrushes *Cinclosoma.* The ground-babblers are confined to the Australasian region, with the exception of a rail-babbler *E. macrocercus* that lives in the forests of Malaysia.

The jungle-babblers, scimitar-babblers and wren-babblers, tit-babblers and tree-babblers, and a very few of the song-babblers and ground-babblers, build domed ball-like nests of moss and dead leaves which are well hidden on or close to the ground. The majority of the song-babblers build open cup-shaped nests which are hidden in low trees, bushes and creepers, while a few of the ground-babblers, such as the quail-thrushes, build open cup-shaped nests on the ground. The rockfowl differ from other babblers by nesting in small groups and by building cup-shaped nests of mud, plastered to rock faces in caves or under overhangs. It is probable that this colonial habit is related to the localized distribution of suitable caves and cliffs. As would be expected in such a widespread and diverse group as the babblers, there is much variation in the colour and markings of their eggs, and in the size of their clutches. Several species particularly song-babblers, are co-operative breeders, but only to the extent that a number of adults, often as many as half a dozen, assist in the feeding of a brood of young. In babblers only one female

lays eggs in any one nest, though in some other species that co-operate two or more females may contribute to a clutch.

Many babblers, particularly those that live in forest, are prominent members of mixed species flocks, which increases the foraging efficiency of the member species. For example, in the forests of Borneo as many as a dozen or more species of babblers may forage together, often with other insectivorous species as well. Each species forages in a particular niche to which it is adapted and in which it forages most efficiently. However, each species is so specialized that it seems incapable of showing much plasticity in its foraging behaviour. Thus a babbler that characteristically forages in green foliage in a stratum 10–15 ft (300–450 cm) above the ground will frequently fail to pursue disturbed insects that escape into other forest strata, even though these may be plainly visible only a short distance away. In these circumstances the foraging of individual birds, or even monospecific flocks, is likely to be very inefficient, for many insects will escape into other niches. On the other hand, several species occupying different niches but hunting together will flush insects from one niche to another to the mutual advantage of all members of the foraging flock. FAMILY: Muscicapidae, ORDER: Passeriformes, CLASS: Aves.   M.P.L.F.

BABIRUSA *Babyrousa babyrossa,* a large almost hairless hog with a brownish-grey rough skin. The head and body length is 34–42 in (86·4–106·7 cm); height at shoulder is 25–31 in (63·5–78·7 cm). The tail is 10·8–12·5 in (27·4–31·7 cm). The nose is typically hog-like with a cartilaginous mobile disk. There are four toes on each foot with the centre two functional and the outer two forming dew claws. The dental formula is as follows: incisors $\frac{2}{3}$; canines $\frac{1}{1}$; premolars $\frac{2}{2}$; molars $\frac{3}{3}\times2=34$. Unlike other members of the family the upper tusks in males go up through the top of the muzzle and curve slightly backwards. The lower tusks do not touch the upper tusks and extend outward.

The babirusa is limited to the Celebes and Molucca Islands including Toguin, Buru and the Sulu Islands.

Information on breeding is scarce. In the London Zoo captive females have given birth to single young in January, March and April following a 125–150 day gestation period.

Babirusa inhabit dense damp forests and bamboo thickets. Like most other hogs, they are social animals and travel in small groups. They feed mostly on fruits, green vegetation, roots and tubers. FAMILY: Suidae, SUBORDER: Suiformes, ORDER: Artiodactyla, CLASS: Mammalia.

Portrait of a young baboon.

BABOONS, typical open-country monkeys of Africa, distinguished by their long muzzle, especially in the male, and their large size. The most widespread species, *Papio hamadryas,* is distributed all over the savannah, semi-desert and lightly forested regions of Africa south of the Sahara. There are also two species in the thick forests of the Cameroun region with very short tails, brightly coloured buttocks and heavy ridges on either side of the nose. Savannah baboons are not highly coloured, have no strong ridges, and their tails curve up, back and down in an arc.

It was once thought there were five species of baboon in the savannah areas, each confined to a portion of the range; but recent studies have demonstrated the existence of intergradation between them, with hybrid troops and clines of colour and hair patterns through the range. To the north they are more stocky, the males have big manes, the face juts and the pointed nose extends beyond the end of the muzzle. They are light in colour the

hairs being banded dark and light. To the south baboons are more long-legged and rangy, the male has little or no mane, the face is more bent downwards, and the nose does not overhang the end of the muzzle. The colour is darker and the hair less banded. Eight subspecies are recognized:

Hamadryas, Mantled or Sacred baboon *P. hamadryas hamadryas*. Rather small, 2½ ft (76 cm) long, tail 2 ft (61 cm), weight up to 40 lb (18 kg); females brown, males grey; males with huge mane which ends in middle of back, very short hair on rest of body. Face pinkish, ischial callosities red. Northern Somalia, Eritrea and southwestern Arabia.

Olive baboon *P. h. anubis*. Much larger, olive-green; male with long mane. Face and ischial callosities black. Senegal east to Ethiopia and Kenya, intergrades with Hamadryas along Awash river, northern Ethiopia.

Guinea baboon *P. h. papio*. Smaller, maned, reddish, with red ischial callosities. Restricted to small area of Senegal, Guinea and Gambia. Yellow baboon *P. h. cynocephalus*. Long-legged, no mane, yellowish. East Africa, from Amboseli (where intergrades with Olive baboon) to Zambezi.

Dwarf baboon *P. h. kindae*. Like Yellow baboon but much smaller and short-faced; Zambia and Katanga.

Kalahari chacma baboon *P. h. ruacana*. Variegated, brownish, long face and long crest of hair on nape and withers. Southern Angola and Southwest Africa.

Grey-footed chacma *P. h. griseipes*. Dark yellowish, larger than Kalahari chacma, otherwise similar. Rhodesia and Mozambique; intergrades with Yellow baboon in eastern Zambia.

Black-footed chacma *P. h. ursinus*. Blackish brown, with black hands and feet; largest of all baboons. South Africa, except for northern Transvaal.

Baboons, aggressive and dangerous, live in large troops whose composition and social behaviour vary from area to area. In the savannahs of East and South Africa the troops are smallish with 20–80 animals and each troop stays together all the time. However, in the desert areas of Eritrea, northern Somalia and Southwest Africa, huge troops are found, as many as 150 together, but these split up during the day into one-male units and bachelor bands. This latter type of society, typical especially of Hamadryas baboons, has a number of special features and must be described separately; the more typical savannah type of social organization will be described first.

Savannah baboons have a more or less hierarchical organization within the troop, a single male often being dominant in all respects. However, different individuals may appear to dominate in different situations and sometimes two or three of the less strong males may constantly associate together and take precedence in situations where a single stronger male would otherwise always dominate. Females are always subordinate to males, and have a kind of rank order amongst themselves, although this too may be broken:

Baboons feeding at the edge of a forest in East Africa in company with antelopes.

for example, a female with a young infant is treated with consideration by the rest of the troop.

Within the baboon troop the sex ratio is more or less equal; there are, however, two or three times as many adult females as there are adult males, since females mature at 4—5 years, males only after 7—10 years. The troop has a wide home range, with a core area consisting of a clump of trees. Around this, the troop wanders within a radius of a mile or more, and may travel as much as 6 miles in a day, foraging as they go. Baboons are omnivorous. They feed on seeds, tubers, grass, insects—even scorpions and snakes. Baboons have also been observed to kill and eat young gazelles; they do not stalk them with intent as chimpanzees do, however, but probably merely stumble on a baby gazelle that has been left lying in the grass by its mother.

By day a baboon troop will often associate with a herd of ungulates, especially impala. The association is mutually beneficial: the impala are alert and give warning of danger, while the baboons are powerful and fearsome, and can offer protection to the antelopes. Leopards and cheetahs are not infrequently turned away by a group of male baboons. On the other hand, a lone baboon, even a male, may be killed and eaten by a leopard. On the Serengeti, baboons form 4% of the leopard's diet.

The baboon troop is very tightly knit; an individual very rarely changes troops. A very big, unwieldy troop will split into subgroups for foraging, and gradually two independent troops will result. Dominant males and females with infants travel in the centre of a troop; younger and weaker males tend to move along the edges, and are the first to see and warn of danger. When this happens the big adult males move forward. Like all Old

Baby baboon riding pick-a-back.

World monkeys, a male baboon's canines are long, sharp and fearsome, with a razor edge up the back.

The female's sexual cycle lasts 35 days. Like many higher Primates, female baboons develop sexual swellings; the skin around the vulva begins to swell, filling with a watery fluid, soon after menstruation, and is at its maximum at the height of oestrus. At this period, the dominant male will mate with her and try to prevent other males from doing so. Hence, most of the next generation are the offspring of the strongest male. After oestrus, the swelling rapidly goes down, and the ranking male no longer holds a monopoly over her; other males can and do mate with females out of oestrus.

Gestation lasts six months; the infant is born black, and is a focus of solicitous attention from other troop members. At first it rides on its mother's belly, later on her back. After four to six months the infant changes to the adult colouration and a little later is weaned. Gradually, as the youngster becomes more and more independent of its mother, it

begins to run to the adult males for protection instead. The rather rough play of juveniles is tolerated at first by the adult males, and gradually more and more corrective training, in the form of cuffs and threats, are brought to bear. Young males soon become very pugnacious, and severe fights often break out among them, presumably in attempts to establish future dominance. The adult males are, however, quick to break up these fights and chase and threaten the participants. They also in this way punish a subadult who is annoying a female or an infant, and an infant's squeal will invariably bring several big males rushing over to protect it.

Apart from being the protectors and the reproductively successful animals, dominant males are yielded right of way by the others. They get the food if there is a shortage and they give more threats than they receive. A threatening stare or a drawing back of the lips to reveal the canines, with a jerking crouch and coughing grunt, the 'open-mouth threat', is generally sufficient to instil good behaviour into a miscreant. Subordinate behaviour takes several forms. One of the commonest is 'presenting', a pseudo-sexual action which invites the dominant animal to mount, and even thrust, although no penetration is usually achieved, and often enough the dominant animal has no erection. Males as well as females present in subordination situations.

Sexual mounting and actual copulation take different forms in different races of baboon. In most, there is a single mount, the male thrusting until he has achieved ejaculation. However, in the Black-footed chacma the dominant male and an oestrus female may form a consort pair, foraging and moving around together for part of the day; the male mounts and gives a few thrusts, then dismounts, remounting again after a couple of minutes; this goes on until ejaculation occurs. Chacmas also mate with more vocalizations than other baboons.

The big troops of Hamadryas baboons, which gather every night on the sleeping cliffs, split up during the day into a number of smaller groups each consisting of an adult male and several females, and the surplus males form a bachelor band. The situation has been well studied by Hans Kummer. In each one-male unit, the male threatens his females, and they gather around him and follow closely. They have to be taught to do this; an animal's usual reaction on being threatened is to flee. Kummer and his associates found that Olive baboon females released into Hamadryas areas would be rounded up by Hamadryas males and would quickly learn to follow them. It is thus that, in spite of the differing social organisations of Olive and Hamadryas baboons, there is

Troop of Olive baboons spread out foraging, ready to move to cover if danger threatens.

The male Olive baboon with cape-like mane.

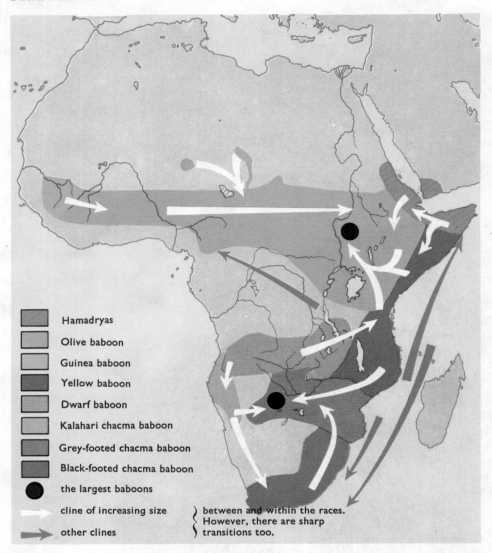

Hamadryas
Olive baboon
Guinea baboon
Yellow baboon
Dwarf baboon
Kalahari chacma baboon
Grey-footed chacma baboon
Black-footed chacma baboon
● the largest baboons
⟶ cline of increasing size   } between and within the races.
⟶ other clines   } However, there are sharp
                                    } transitions too.

Map showing the distribution of the eight subspecies of Hamadryas baboon, with arrows indicating the clines of colour, hair patterns and size.

considerable interbreeding on the borders of their ranges, since each female learns to adapt to the behaviour of the local male. A disobedient female among Hamadryas will be disciplined with a neck-bite—a quick bite on the nape administered by the male, using his incisors.

Herding behaviour in Hamadryas begins early, at three or four years of age. Previously a young male will have mated with mature females, and finally the herding and the sexual instincts of the young male fuse when one of the females he has herded becomes his sexual partner, and the nucleus of his one-male unit. The bachelor males tend to associate with particular one-male groups, and are always on the look-out for a chance to take over the group.

Although Olive baboons penetrate far into the forests of the northeastern Congo, the real forest baboons are the Short-tailed drill *Papio leucophaeus* and the mandrill *P. sphinx*. Mandrills are even larger than most baboons, dark brown with white cheek-

Yellow baboon in typical squatting posture.

fringes, a yellow beard, and tuft of hair on the crown. The face is brilliantly coloured in the adult male: the nose is red, the ridges on either side of it blue. In females and young the same colours are present, but much duller. The penis is red and the scrotum is blue; the ischial callosities are red, and the buttock hair blue and white. The maxillary ridges are diagonally grooved. The drill is smaller than the mandrill, more olive in colour, with a black face and no grooves on the muzzle ridges; the chin is red; there is a white fringe all round the face.

The mandrill lives in Cameroun, Equatorial Guinea, Gabon and the Congo (Brazzaville), mainly near the coast. The drill is found in the same areas but prefers more inland forests, and extends onto Mt. Cameroun, the Cross River district of Nigeria, and the island of Fernando Po. Both live mainly on the forest floor but do not hesitate to climb trees, eating fruit and berries as well as bark and roots. The troops are large, up to 60 in number, but split into one-male parties at times (at least in the drill), which forage separately for several days. Intertroop location signals are given as they come back together again.

The drill and mandrill are sometimes placed in a separate genus from the more typical, open-country baboons. However recent studies indicate that they are essentially similar, merely being specialized for forest life by developing a large, grasping great toe and big cutting incisors. Baboons are regarded as pests in most parts of their range, and are hunted for the damage they do to crops and gardens. There is at present, however, no danger that they will become scarce. FAMILY: Cercopithecidae, ORDER: Primates, CLASS: Mammalia   C.P.G.

BACKSWIMMERS, common name for a group of aquatic bugs. They resemble waterboatmen, family Corixidae, in general appearance, for their body is boat-shaped and streamlined and they swim by using their long hindlegs as paddles. However, they differ from waterboatmen in swimming on their backs and are vicious predators often attacking and killing animals larger than themselves, including young fish. The sharp stylets in their mouthparts can inflict painful wounds and they should be handled carefully. FAMILY: Notonectidae, CLASS: Insecta, PHYLUM: Arthropoda.

BADGERS, medium-sized members of the weasel family Mustelidae, well known for their digging habits. Badgers comprise six genera which are distributed over North America, Eurasia and Indonesia as far as Borneo. The South African ratel is sometimes included as a seventh genus. The name is derived from the French *becheur*, meaning digger or gardener. All badgers are heavily

Backswimmer, photographed from below, showing reflection in water's surface.

covers a wide range of vegetable and animal matter, showing great seasonal and local variations. Voles, hedgehogs, moles may be eaten as well as smaller frogs, slugs, beetles and above all, earthworms. Fruits of every kind, maize, wheat and even fungi are also taken when available. The badger's role as a predator of poultry and lambs has been disputed over the years and it would seem that only under very special circumstances is a 'rogue' badger inclined to tackle such a difficult prey.

The badger is extremely wary, spending long minutes sniffing the air before emerging shortly after dusk. Should it be disturbed at that time, it may retreat underground for several hours before attempting another exit. When the coast is clear, the badgers come out one by one and usually spend long minutes scratching and grooming themselves, no longer confined in their movements. Cubs may be observed playing leapfrog or king-of-the-castle, and sometimes the adults join in. Well worn trails lead to the foraging grounds with numerous scenting spots along

A pair of European badgers *Meles meles* leaving their set at nightfall.

built animals and their muscular legs appear even shorter than they are, due to the thickness of the coarse fur. The tail, usually shorter than in other mustelids, is 1–8 in (2–20 cm) long. All badgers have potent anal scent glands which appear to be particularly effective in the Oriental Stink badgers *Mydaus* and *Suillotaxus,* Considerable size and colour variations exist. Three genera, *Meles, Taxidea* and *Melogale,* have distinct black and white facial 'masks' contrasting with the inconspicuous salt-and-pepper grey of the back and the black underparts and legs. Badgers usually excavate their burrows or sets where there is sufficient cover, in woodland or, in drier areas, brushland, and choose sandy limestone or clay. The European badger *Meles meles* is gregarious and the sets may become, with successive generations, an extensive maze of tunnels up to 100 ft (30 m) long, leading to chambers lined with a 'bedding' of leaves or grass. Sometimes up to ten entrances and exits can be discovered but usually only two or three are in use at one time. Small ventilation holes air the tunnels closest to the surface. Dry bundles of bedding are collected, either pushed or carried backwards into the set, clasped in the forearms, the badger shuffling along on elbows and hind-feet. Bedding may also be nosed to the surface during the night and spread around the set to air, then gathered again before daybreak. Not only do badgers keep the set clean underground but they also dig shallow pits nearby where dung is deposited.

The diet of this omnivorous mammal

The American badger *Taxidea taxus* lives on open plains.

the way which serve both as territorial boundaries and as a means of finding the way back to the set in the darkness.

The European badger is found in Eurasia down to southern China. Males are slightly larger than females measuring 27–40 in (67–100 cm) and weighing 22–55 lb (10–25 kg), depending on the season. Large layers of fat are present in autumn. Hibernation occurs only in the colder areas of their range. Breeding usually occurs in spring or late summer, but there is delayed implantation varying from 2–10 months. The embryo develops for a few days, then lies dormant and is not implanted in the uterus until much later. The cubs are born in February or March. Numbering two to four, the blind cubs remain in a nesting chamber for several weeks. When they first emerge two months later, they move cautiously about, staying close to the mother, starting at the slightest sound or strange smell. European badgers make a variety of sounds. A short warning note may change into a growl or into a bark if the animal is startled suddenly. Contact sounds are low and throaty and when aroused a very loud scream is given.

The American badger *Taxidea taxus* occurs throughout the drier regions of the United States down to southern Mexico. Stockier than the European badger, it appears to be even more 'flattened'. The black and white facial stripes are narrower and less distinct. Measuring 21–35 in (52–87 cm) and weighing 8–22 lb (3·5–10 kg), they are usually smaller than the European badger. Unlike its European counterpart, the American badger is solitary most of the year and does not use the same burrow generation

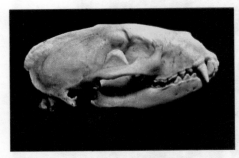

Badger's skull: the lower jaw is hinged to the skull and cannot be removed without breaking the bone.

after generation. Breeding takes places in late summer and delayed implantation occurs, so that the cubs are not born until the following April. Weaned at six weeks, the young become independent by late autumn and set off on their own for the winter.

The hog-badger *Arctonyx collaris* is found from India to Sumatra and up into China. More upstanding, albeit stout, this species nevertheless retains the same stocky appearance, with formidable claws. A large hog-badger measures approximately 32 in (80 cm) overall and weighs 25 lb (11 kg). The most distinguishing characteristic is the long, mobile snout, used in foraging for grubs and insects. Although its range overlaps that of the European badger, the hog-badger seems even more secretive and the two species do not compete.

The Malayan Stink badger *Mydaus javanensis* and the Palawan Stink badger *Suillotaxus marchei* are the rarest members of this group. The Malayan species which occurs also in Sumatra, Java and Borneo has an overall dark brown or black colouration.

The Bornean ferret badger *Melogale orientalis* is widespread from Nepal to Borneo and three species are currently recognized. This is the smallest badger, measuring 19–25 in (48–63 cm), the bushy tail accounting for a third of the total length. This cat-sized animal seems to be a compromise between a lumbering badger and a nimble ferret. Unlike the other badgers it has been reported to climb trees. However it shares omnivorous tendencies and burrowing habits with other badgers. FAMILY: Mustelidae, ORDER: Carnivora, CLASS: Mammalia. N.D.

BADGER SKULLS, can be told at a glance from those of other mammals of a comparable size. In most mammals the lower jaw falls away from the skull when the flesh is removed but that of the badger is so hinged that it cannot be dislocated without breaking the strong bony socket which encloses the jaw articulation. The skull of the badger is also extremely heavily built with a high bony ridge on the cranium for the attachment of strong muscles. Altogether the skull gives the impression of great strength and power, yet badgers prefer to feed on soft food such as earthworms, beetles and fruit. The strong hinge seems unnecessary but it is also found in the badger's smaller relatives such as weasels and stoats which need a well-anchored jaw when attacking prey, such as rabbits, larger than themselves.

BAER K. E. von, 1792–1876. German pioneer of embryology, born in Estonia. In 1826 he discovered (by accident) the mammalian ovum in the ovary of a bitch. He also demonstrated the similarities between the early embryonic stages in different vertebrates, and discovered the notochord—the gelatinous tube formed in the dorsal region of all vertebrate embryos.

BALANCE OF NATURE, a concept which in the latter half of the 19th and early 20th centuries saw 'Nature' as resting in a state of stable equilibrium with completely integrated relationships between plants and animals. Understanding of the term has now altered considerably and recent development of accurate ecological methods for assessing the role and function of organisms in relation to their environment has revealed that animal species show far greater population fluctuations than would be expected from a study of the animal community as a whole. A degree of balance does exist, but it is a highly dynamic and unstable state as a result of the closely linked relationships of organisms, not only to one another, but also to non-biological factors such as the climate and the availability of essential minerals and trace elements. The numbers of animals of

Map showing distribution of the species of badgers.

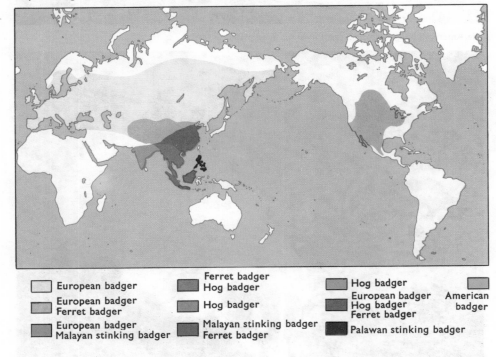

☐ European badger	Ferret badger
	Hog badger
European badger Ferret badger	Hog badger
European badger Malayan stinking badger	Malayan stinking badger Ferret badger
	Hog badger
	European badger Hog badger Ferret badger
American badger	
	Palawan stinking badger

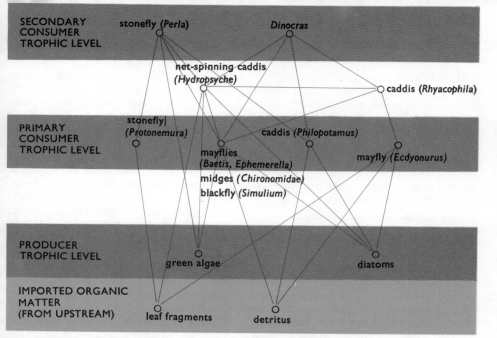

SECONDARY CONSUMER TROPHIC LEVEL
stonefly (*Perla*)   *Dinocras*

net-spinning caddis (*Hydropsyche*)
caddis (*Rhyacophila*)

PRIMARY CONSUMER TROPHIC LEVEL
stonefly (*Protonemura*)   caddis (*Philopotamus*)
mayflies (*Baetis, Ephemerella*)   mayfly (*Ecdyonurus*)
midges (*Chironomidae*)
blackfly (*Simulium*)

PRODUCER TROPHIC LEVEL
green algae   diatoms

IMPORTED ORGANIC MATTER (FROM UPSTREAM)
leaf fragments   detritus

Portion of food web in a small stream community of South Wales, showing the three trophic levels, the interlocking of food chains to form the food web, the fact that organisms, such as *Hydropsyche*, may occupy an intermediate position between major trophic levels and an 'open' system in which part of the basic food is imported from outside the stream.

different species do not remain constant but fluctuate as a result of the complex interaction of numerous environmental factors bringing about an increased or decreased natality or mortality.

The availability of food has the greatest influence in determining the optimum numbers of animals in a particular habitat. The trophic (feeding) relationships of organisms may be illustrated by food webs such as that shown for part of a small stream community:

Most food webs are far too complex to show in their entirety but this example illustrates the interlocking nature of food chains, the intermediate trophic position of some animals known as omnivores, between herbivores and carnivores and how animals usually obtain food from a number of different sources. The more an animal specializes in its food preferences, the more it reduces competition for food with other animals but the greater are the chances that it may starve under adverse conditions or increase and over-exploit its food resources when conditions are favourable. In addition to competition for food, both between individuals and between species, a number of other factors are important in maintaining animal populations below a level where they could exceed the food resources of the habitat and bring about a population decline, even to the point of extinction. Competition for mates and breeding space, favourable and adverse conditions during the breeding season, abnormal climatic conditions and varying intensities of predation at different stages of the life-cycle are important factors controlling the density of animal species. The same regulatory factors rarely affect different species in the same way so that a degree of

balance is maintained in the animal community in relation to its food resources.

In areas of the world where food chains are comparatively simple, for example the northern tundras, insufficient control mechanisms may be operating to prevent periodic population explosions of animals. The population cycles of the lemming and its predators, the Arctic fox and Snowy owl, are classical examples. Every three or four years, over enormous areas of the tundras, the lemmings become extremely abundant, only to show an abrupt decline, often within a single season, as a result of their overgrazing the vegetation representing both their food and shelter. The foxes and owls which feed on the lemmings increase as their prey increases only to be similarly reduced to very low populations as the lemmings die of starvation. The foxes starve in large numbers while the owls migrate south in search of food. When the vegetation recovers the few remaining lemmings have large food resources available to them with few predators present to control their numbers, so that the cycle is perpetuated.

A number of elements and their dissolved salts cycle between living organisms and their environment. Decomposer organisms, particularly fungi and bacteria, play an essential role in these cycles by breaking down plant and animal materials so that the nutrients can be re-utilized for plant production. The removal of large quantities of organic material from these cycles, by erosion, poor agricultural practice, or the inhibition of the decomposition processes for long periods of time, can result in deficiencies of the major nutrients such as nitrogen, potassium, sulphur, calcium, phosphorus and so forth, and particularly the trace-

elements such as cobalt, copper and molybdenum. These nutrients must be available in balanced proportions; too much or too little of any one of them may limit plant productivity and hence affect the dependant animal population. Phytoplankton (unicellular plants) and zooplankton (predominantly small Crustacea) in the surface waters of lakes and seas show linked population cycles, like those of the lemming and its predators, in relation to the availability of mineral nutrients in the water. As these nutrients become scarce, having been incorporated into plant and animal tissues, the plankton populations decline and their bodies sink to the lake or sea bed where bacterial action releases the nutrients. Seasonal upwellings of the nutrient-rich waters to the surface, brought about by wind or thermal effects, promote new phytoplankton blooms, followed by a rapid increase in the zooplankton. When the nutrients are exhausted the populations die and the cycle is repeated.

Many natural communities have become unstable or have been destroyed by man's industry, agriculture and disposal of sewage. Poor agricultural methods have turned good land into dust-bowls; sewage has been added to many of our lakes and rivers, promoting excessive algal and bacterial growths, deoxygenation of the water and the exclusion of higher animals and plants. The use of pesticides to protect man's crops has had serious consequences, not only on the destructive pests. There are numerous cases where the use of insecticides has caused the destruction of beneficial insect parasites resulting in an explosive increase of pests the year after application. In other cases honeybees have been destroyed after spraying fields and orchards, with disastrous consequences to commercial fruit crops pollinated by these insects. Certain pesticides, particularly DDT and Dieldrin, which remain active for long periods of time, can become incorporated into food chains, and then concentrated in the body tissues of predators at the top of the feeding hierarchy, frequently resulting in infertility or death. Many hawks and owls have died as a result of these insecticides and consequently vole populations have increased in some parts of Britain damaging forestry plantations.

The interrelationships of organisms maintaining the balance of nature are so complex that extensive study is necessary to foresee the consequences of a small imbalance induced by man. Unfortunately man rarely appreciates the state of balance until adversely affected by the imbalance resulting from his own activities. J.M.A.

BALANTIDIUM, a genus of one-celled ciliates, commonly parasitic in cockroaches, amphibians and mammals. Most frogs, toads and newts in Europe and elsewhere harbour

Bald eagle

several species of *Balantidium* in their small and large intestines. In British amphibians the species are *Balantidium duodeni* in the small intestine and *B. entozoon* and *B. elongatum* in the large intestine or rectum. Among mammals *B. caviae* is very common in Guinea pigs and *B. coli* occurs in pigs and also in man. This is the only ciliate recorded in man and it is seldom encountered. *B. coli* is common throughout the world in pigs and apparently lives harmlessly in their guts, causing no disease. Man acquires the parasite after close contact with the pig, presumably ingesting encysted ciliates, and may develop ulcers resembling those caused by *Entamoeba histolytica*. It is almost certain that the successful invasion of the human intestine depends on some degree of nutritional deficiency on the part of the host. In Britain, for example, only about six cases have been recorded and in the United States there are only a few more, but many more records come from underdeveloped countries. All members of the genus possess a uniform covering of cilia and a well developed mouth at the anterior end. The macronucleus is typically kidney-shaped and there are usually two contractile vacuoles. ORDER: Trichomstomatida, CLASS: Ciliata, PHYLUM: Protozoa.   F.E.G.C.

Bald eagle, America's national emblem.

BALD EAGLE *Haliaetus leucocephalus,* a very large sea eagle confined to North American coasts, lakes and rivers, and the American national emblem. It feeds by fishing or by robbing other birds. Two races occur, one in central and southern United States, the other in Alaska and western Canada. The Florida population breeds in winter and migrates north in hot summers. The Alaskan birds feed largely on dead and dying Pacific salmon for part of the year. Formerly common, it is now much reduced in central-south USA through shooting (despite national status) and pesticide poisoning. It breeds in trees, making huge nests, laying two or three eggs and rearing one or two young per year. FAMILY: Accipitridae, ORDER: Falconiformes, CLASS: Aves.

BALD EAGLE, the Bald eagle did not become the National Emblem of the United States without argument. Benjamin Franklin criticized it for being 'like those men who live by sharping and robbing', a reference to its habit of stealing fish from ospreys. Franklin's choice was the wild turkey, apparently a more virtuous bird but it is difficult to imagine a turkey posing so nobly as the Bald eagle on the seal of the United States.

BALEEN, or whalebone, the fibrous plates that hang in rows from the roof of the mouth of Whalebone whales and used for straining food from the water. (See Whalebone whales). For many years baleen was a very valuable source of income to the whalers because, before plastics and spring steel were invented, there was nothing to touch baleen for elasticity combined with strength. Thus it was used for countless purposes in machinery and in domestic articles such as corsets, whips, umbrellas and the peaks of caps. In the 17th century it cost about £1,200 to equip a ship for whaling and a single Greenland right whale yielded about $1\frac{1}{2}$ tons of baleen, alone worth over £2,000. Artificial materials such as plastics have replaced baleen, which is now the only part of the whale not utilized in a modern whale factory, but it is still used for a few purposes such as in riding crops and guardsmen's bearskins.

BALI OX, a domesticated form of the *banteng used as cattle on the island of Bali, Indonesia.

BAMBOO WORMS, polychaete annelid worms found in mud or muddy sand between tidemarks or below low-tide level. They owe their name to the form of the segments, which are long and narrow so that the whole body is rather bamboo-like. Most are small or very small, but a few are as much as 4 in (10 cm) or so in length. Creamy, pink, reddish or with reddish markings on the body, the bamboo worms may be recognized by the anal funnel or crown. These animals lie vertically in the mud or sand, sometimes within a sandy tube made from mucus-compacted sand grains, with the head downwards. The anal crown lies just below the surface. The head has no special features and indeed often looks as if it has been sawn off obliquely.

Bamboo worms may be found all over the world and extend from the sea-shore to great depths in the sea. They are rarely common and are not often seen by the casual observer, but they do sometimes form quite dense colonies where they do occur. The sexes are separate, the eggs and sperm being shed into the sea where fertilization occurs.

The fertilized eggs develop into free-swimming larvae which later settle on an appropriate substratum and develop into the adult form. Thereafter they do not normally leave the mud in which they live, feeding upside down and casting the mud which passes through the gut onto the surface. They respire by drawing water in and out of their burrows or tubes rather like a syringe. *Chymenella torquata* is common on the Atlantic coast of the United States. FAMILY: Maldanidae, ORDER: Phyllodocida, CLASS: Polychaeta, PHYLUM: Annelida.   R.P.D.

BANANAQUIT *Coereba flaveola,* a small, 4 in (10 cm), grey and bright-yellow bird with a conspicuous white eye-stripe and a rather long decurved bill. It is widespread in tropical America from the West Indies, where it is probably the commonest bird, south to Argentina and Paraguay. The bananaquit has adjusted well to man and is now found both in the native forests and in gardens, plantations and cleared areas. It feeds on fruit, nectar and insects. It constructs many domed nests, some of which are used for nesting and others for roosting. FAMILY: Coerebidae, ORDER: Passeriformes, CLASS: Aves.

BANDED ANT-EATER *Myrmecobius fasciatus* or numbat, a pouchless, termite-eating marsupial which lives in the fallen hollow limbs of wandoo trees *Eucalyptus redunca* in southwestern Australia. The numbat shares common features of behaviour, reproduction and chromosome cytology with the marsupial 'cats' and their allies to which it is undoubtedly closely related in spite of numerous aberrant features of dentition. Adult animals are rat-sized and weigh about 1 lb (454 gm).

The coat of the numbat is coarse but it is none the less a remarkably beautiful animal having bright rusty-red fur broken by six or seven creamy white bars across the hind part of the body. The head is flat above, the nose of the adult animals long and pointed and the tail long and wand-like especially when, as sometimes happens, it is held above the body with the hairs erect. There are five toes on the forefeet and four on the hindfeet. The skull is broad and expanded with four incisors, a single canine and three premolar teeth on each side of the upper jaw. As in all dasyurid marsupials the lower jaw has only three incisor teeth and the same number of canines and premolars as in the upper jaw. Unlike most other marsupials, however the numbat has more than four molar teeth in each jaw and they are reduced in size and degenerate in accord with the insectivorous mode of feeding. There may be as many as six molars in each jaw giving a total of about 50 teeth.

The numbat is found today in scattered

The Banded ant-eater or numbat in its natural habitat. Once thought to be a dying race it is now recovering its numbers.

areas of suitable habitat over a total area of about 10,000 sq miles (26,000 sq km) in southwestern Australia. It was formerly known from a much wider area with its easternmost limit on the Murray River about 1,500 miles (2,500 km) east of its present habitat. A second form, the Rusty numbat *Myrmecobius fasciatus rufus,* has been described from desert country in the northwest of South Australia.

The male numbat is fertile only at certain times of the year. Mating takes place from midsummer to early autumn and the young, two to four in number, are born between January and May. The female numbat is entirely pouchless but the young become firmly attached to the teats, carried below the mother's body in the pelvic region. The young grip the mother's fur with the clawed digits of their forelimbs to assist attachment. The time spent suckling on the teat is long by marsupial standards, approaching six months. The young are left in a nest in a hollow branch of a tree, or in a depression in the ground, during the latter part of the lactation cycle in August and September, while the mother feeds. They are seen abroad foraging in October, November and December and may begin breeding when about a year old.

The habitat of the numbat is governed by the presence of wandoo and other trees which provide fallen limbs with their centres eaten out by the termite *Copotermes acinaciformis.* This termite, the most destructive known in Australia, is the chief food of the

numbat but its scats contain remains of about 20 other sorts of termites and a greater number of kinds of ants. The food is obtained by digging in the upper 2 in (5 cm) of soil and by turning over small pieces of wood under which termites and ants live.

The young animal does not have the elongated snout of the adult and the pre-orbital region of the skull shows marked positive allometric growth in post-weaning stages, that is, it grows at a relatively much faster rate than the remainder of the body. FAMILY: Dasyuridae, ORDER: Marsupialia, CLASS: Mammalia.   G.B.S.

BANDICOOT, a rabbit-sized *marsupial,* insect and small-animal eater with carnivorous dentition, as in Native cats, but with the same foot structure as in kangaroos and wallabies (syndactylous). The bandicoots have many unique features and their earliest fossil history is unknown so relationships with the other marsupials are problematical although they are perhaps most nearly related to the dasyurids (Native cats, etc). They have pointed ears and tapering snouts.

The name 'bandicoot' was apparently first applied to large rodents (genus *Bandicota)* which inhabit southern Asia. The word means 'pig-rat' in Telugu, a Dravidian language of India. The marsupial bandicoots are quadrupedal, but with the hindlimbs enlarged and carrying most of the body weight, while the forelimbs are used for scratching and digging. The insect food is mainly taken from the top few inches of soil or from

rotting wood on the surface of the ground. Bandicoots show a remarkable amount of growth after sexual maturity and the 20 or so species cannot be separated by size alone. The smallest bandicoot is *Microperoryctes* of west New Guinea Mountains, less than 1 ft (30 cm) long, with a hindfoot length of 1·2 in (3 cm), while the largest forms of Shortnosed and Rabbit-eared bandicoots are up to 2½ ft (75 cm) long and have foot lengths three times greater. The tail is much shorter than the body length in all except Rabbit-eared bandicoots. The predominant dentition of five upper and three lower incisor teeth in each jaw and the greatly elongated nasal region of the skull distinguish bandicoots from other marsupials. There are well-developed canines and three premolar and four molar teeth in each jaw; the deciduous premolar is minute and less than a third the size of the third premolar which replaces it.

Although the methods of reproduction are typical of marsupials, the considerable differences from other groups indicate that the bandicoots have had a long separate evolution. The female reproductive system has a short urogenital sinus and very long lateral vaginal canals with short culs-de-sac and expanded vaginal caecae. While in the uterus the young are nourished by a complex allantoic placenta, the like of which is found nowhere else amongst marsupials, and the newborn young are much larger than those of Native cats although the total period from mating to birth is only about 12 days. The pouch opens backwards, instead of forwards

The bandicoot, which has earned a bad name by digging on lawns in search of insects.

as in kangaroos, and growth in the pouch is very rapid. The Short-nosed and Long-nosed bandicoots and their New Guinea relatives have a total of only 14 chromosomes including two X sex-chromosomes in females and X and Y sex-chromosomes in males. Both sex-chromosomes are, however, carried only in the germinal tissues of either sex. Body cells of females eliminate one X chromosome and of males the Y chromosome during post-embryonic development.

The Long-nosed bandicoots *Perameles* inhabit the eastern, southern and southwestern coastal areas of Australia and Tasmania and in places extend inland to the arid regions.

The bandicoots of New Guinea and associated islands are included in the genera *Echymipera* (three species), *Peroryctes* (two species), *Rhynchomeles* and *Microperoryctes*. The fifth incisor tooth of the upper jaw has been lost in *Echymipera* and *Rhynchomeles*. *Echymipera rufescens*, alone amongst New Guinea forms, has reached the mainland of Australia on the Cape York Peninsula.

The Short-nosed bandicoots *Isoodon* occur, or occurred, throughout the Australian mainland, on many off-shore islands, and one species of the typically Australian group is found also in New Guinea. Both Short-and Long-nosed bandicoots occupy concealed nests made beneath mounds of grass, leaves, sticks, etc.

The Pig-footed bandicoot *Chaeropus*, now perhaps extinct, is probably at least partially adapted to a herbivorous diet. This remarkable animal has only two functional toes on the forefeet and one on the hindfeet. It once occurred sparsely over a wide area of Australian desert country.

The Rabbit-eared bandicoots *Macrotis* are desert-dwelling animals which live in

burrows from 3–6 ft (1–2 m) deep. These animals have many morphological differences from the Short- and Long-nosed and New Guinea bandicoots. They have only four (instead of five) toes on the hindfeet, a long tail, large ears and beautiful silky fur. They have a multiple sex-chromosome sex-determining mechanism; there being two Y and one X chromosome in each of the male cells and two X chromosomes in each of the female cells. There are more chromosomes than in other bandicoots and the sex chromosomes are not eliminated from body cells. FAMILY: Peramelidae, ORDER: Marsupialia, CLASS: Mammalia.   G.B.S.

BANDY-BANDY *Vermicella annulata*, a small venomous snake found throughout most parts of continental Australia, from the wet coastal forests to the central deserts. Up to 3 ft (0·9 m) long the bandy-bandy is a slender, small-headed snake with up to 70 alternate black and white bands along its length. It is a burrowing snake which forages above ground at night, feeding on insects, small lizards and especially Blind snakes. It is, however, not regarded as dangerous to humans or domestic animals because it has small fangs and a mild venom. When threat-

Bandy-bandy, relatively harmless Australian snake.

ened the bandy-bandy exhibits a distinctive behaviour pattern in which it throws its body into a series of stiffly-held loops. FAMILY: Elapidae, ORDER: Squamata, CLASS: Reptilia.

BANTENG *Bos javanicus*, species of wild ox in Southeast Asia, closely related to the gaur. Banteng are smaller than gaur, averaging a height of $5\frac{1}{2}$ ft (170 cm), and longer-legged, with a smaller dorsal ridge. Like the gaur, the legs have white 'stockings' but unlike them they also have a white patch on the buttocks. The horns are more angular, averaging 24 in (60 cm) in length in bulls but only 12 in (30 cm) or so in cows. The forehead between the horns is naked and heavily keratinized.

Banteng have a wide but discontinuous distribution. The typical race from Java, *B. j javanicus*, has spreading horns, 25–30 in (60–75 cm) across, and the bulls are shining blue-black, while the cows are tawny. In the Borneo race, *B. j. lowi*, the bulls are chocolate brown with horns that are much more upwardly directed. It is also a much smaller animal. There are no banteng in Sumatra and in Burma, Thailand, Cambodia and Vietnam the local race, *B. j. birmanicus* is normally tawny in both sexes, but in Cambodia about 20% of bulls are blackish, and in peninsula Thailand most bulls are black. Bornean banteng are called temadau; in Burma they are called tsaine; and in Cambodia, ansong. There is some doubt whether truly wild banteng occur in Malaya although there are certainly 70 in Kedah, but these may be feral or recent immigrants from Thailand. Whatever their origin they are sufficiently new to the Malays to be called 'sapi utan' (wild ox).

Banteng are still numerous on the mainland of Southeast Asia and on Borneo, but on Java the encroachment of cultivation and the high human population has reduced their numbers and range, and the Javan race ranks as a threatened form. Probably only 300 survive in Java, most of them being in the Udjung Kulon reserve on the western tip.

Unlike gaur, banteng prefer flat or undulating ground, with light forest and glades of grass and bamboo. They are less timid than gaur, and more often enter cultivated fields. They live in herds of 10–30, but many bulls live solitary lives except in the rut. They are more or less nocturnal, feeding during the night and in the early morning, and lying up in the forest to chew the cud by day. In the monsoon season, they go up into the hills, ascending sometimes to 2,000 ft (600 m), to eat the young bamboo shoots. In the dry season they return to the grassy valleys. The time of the rut differs from place to place; in Burma and Manipur (their northernmost range) they mate in September and October, and calves are born in April and May. Calves are reddish and cows mature in two years, bulls a little later.

In Bali, banteng have long been domesti-cated and form a characteristic breed, which is smaller than the true banteng with a more extensive dewlap and lower dorsal ridge; males are never quite black. In parts of Indonesia the Bali ox is extensively used as a draught animal and for milk. In Bali and Lombok some have run wild. In Java the domestication of the banteng is more recent and domestic banteng are almost indis-tinguishable from wild ones. FAMILY: Bovi-dae, ORDER: Artiodactyla, CLASS: Mam-malia.   C.P.G.

BARBARY APE *Macaca sylvanus,* a Macaque monkey living in northwest Africa, with a small colony on Gibraltar, called an ape because its tail is very small and inconspicuous. See Old World monkeys.

BARBARY SHEEP *Ammotragus lervia,* one of the largest members of the 'goat-sheep' tribe as well as one of the most primitive, which shares characteristics ex-hibited by both sheep and goats.

It is a native of North Africa and inhabits the hot arid mountains from the Red Sea to Morocco. It is a common resident of zoos and has been successfully introduced in southwest USA. Barbary sheep have no preorbital and interdigital glands, but odori-ferous glands on the naked underside of the long tail. In this they resemble goats. The long neck mane and cheek beards they share with the urials, the most primitive of sheep. Their horns are the same shape as those found in the most primitive of urials, in the 'round-horned goats', the west Caucasian ibex, *Capra cylindricornis* and the bharal

Pseudois from Tibet. Adults are rufous-grey in colour with lighter bellies, groins and rears. Barbary sheep have produced fertile and viable offspring with domestic goats, but not with sheep although their blood protein picture resembles that of sheep rather than goats. In their social adaptations they are much like the primitive sheep, but with a more generalized combat behaviour. They clash in a similar way to Mountain sheep and are better horn- and shoulder-wrestlers than these. In addition, they jab with their sharply pointed horns and can inflict severe wounds. In this way they resemble neither sheep nor goats but their ancestors, the goat-antelopes, Rupicaprini. As in the latter, there is little difference in external appear-ance between adult males and females except in size. Four races of Barbary sheep are recognized.

Little is known of the biology of Barbary sheep living in their native Africa. They are desert dwellers capable of feeding on hard shrubbery and grasses and can go a long time without water. However, they are less specialized in grazing than sheep. Of the Barbary sheep introduced into the United States of America, large males have reached a shoulder height of 44 in (112 cm) and a weight of 320 lb (145 kg), while females reached weights up to 140 lb (63 kg). Females matured as early as 16 months of age and, as in most zoological gardens, frequently gave birth to twins and even trip-lets.

The gestation period is 160 days, short for so large a member of its tribe. An unusual feature is that Barbary sheep females can become pregnant while still lactating and nursing a young. The lambing and rutting seasons are rather drawn out as is true of desert sheep, and lambs have been born in captivity at all months of the year. The males are less gregarious than those of sheep or goats. Like these, they pay attention pri-marily to oestrous females during the rut and compete for these. The females tend to be rather aggressive, a characteristic also found in ibex. Unlike sheep or goats, Barbary sheep dig 'wallows' with their horns, throw sand over their shoulders and wallow at least with the front of the body. FAMILY: Bovidae, ORDER: Artiodactyla, CLASS: Mammalia.
                                                V.G.

BARBEL *Barbus barbus,* one of Europe's largest members of the carp-like family Cyprinidae. It is also the only European member of the genus *Barbus* found outside the Danube basin. Like other cyprinids, the barbel is streamlined and a good swimmer, well adapted to the swift waters near weirs and in rapid stretches of rivers. It reaches about 14 lb (over 6 kg) in weight. Its name derives from the four barbels around the mouth.

Barbary sheep, the only wild sheep of Africa, from Morocco to Upper Egypt, has goat-like horns.

Barbets

Pollution has sadly restricted the distribution of the barbel but re-stocking programmes have been fairly successful. In 1955 parts of the English rivers Trent, Welland, Bristol Avon and Severn were stocked with barbel, but only in the latter have they bred freely and expanded their range. FAMILY: Cyprinidae, ORDER: Cypriniformes, CLASS: Pisces.

BARBETS, stocky, powerfully built birds closely related to the honeyguides. The largest is about 12 in (30 cm) long, the smallest $3\frac{1}{2}$ in (9 cm) long. The majority of barbets have relatively large heavy bills, sometimes with serrations or 'teeth' along the cutting edges of the upper mandible. These 'teeth' reach their greatest development in a number of African species, notably the Double-toothed barbet *Lybius bidentatus,* and presumably help in the plucking and manipulation of the fruits upon which these species feed. The feet of barbets are zygodactyl (with two toes pointing forwards, two backwards), as in woodpeckers and all other members of the order, and a number of species regularly clamber about tree trunks and branches in woodpecker fashion. Many barbets are brilliantly coloured, notably the American species and the Oriental barbets of the genus *Megalaima,* the latter being bright green, adorned with gaudy patches of blue, red, yellow and black around the head. The sexes are usually similar, though there is strong sexual dimorphism in some of the American species.

Barbets are so named because the majority have well developed chin and rictal bristles, or conspicuous tufts of feathers over their nostrils. Chin and rictal bristles reach their most extreme development in *Megalaima* and are often as long or longer than the bill. Normally these bristles are spread out in a fan around the bill, but they can be depressed so that they lie thickly along the bill, pointing forwards. Until recently the function of these bristles has been unknown, but now it seems likely that they are sense organs for measuring the size of fruits. Field observations on species of *Megalaima* have shown that when they feed on relatively large fruits the bristles are depressed and come into contact with each fruit as it is gripped by the bill. Some fruits are then rejected, others are swallowed. It is significant that such movements of the bristles are not usually seen when relatively small fruits are being eaten. While it is advantageous for specialized fruit eaters, such as barbets, to feed on fruits that are as large as possible, it seems that the sensory bristles prevent time being wasted in attempts to swallow fruits that are too large, or which might wedge in their throats.

Barbets have a pan-tropical distribution, being found in the tropics of America,

The barbel of the clear-running rivers of Europe feeds only at night.

Africa and Asia as far east as Borneo and Bali. The 76 species of barbets are divided between 13 genera, each genus being endemic to one or other of the three regions. About half the species occur in Africa, while America has fewest species and only two genera. All the American and Oriental species, and many African species, live in tropical forest, this being the typical habitat of the family, but in Africa many barbets range into woodland and savannah. The limiting factor of their distribution is the need for trees large enough to have suitable nesting holes, though species of *Trachyphonus* nest in earth holes in banks and gullies, and consequently range into semi-arid country with only sparsely scattered small trees. Using their powerful bills barbets can ex-

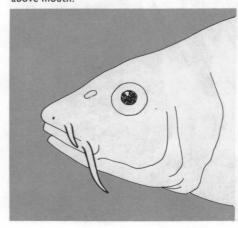

Head of *Barbus* showing two pairs of small barbels above mouth.

cavate their own nest holes but, unlike woodpeckers, they are only capable of working soft, decaying wood. The majority of barbets breed solitarily though species in the African genus *Gymnobucco* breed in small colonies. Outside the breeding season nest holes continue to be used for roosting, and at least one American species, the Prong-billed barbet *Semnornis frantzii,* roosts communally. African barbets are the most frequent hosts for parasitic honeyguides.

Barbets are primarily fruit-eaters, though they supplement their diet with insects when these are readily available, particularly during the breeding season. A few species are predominantly insectivorous. The calls of barbets are often among the most conspicuous bird noises in the areas in which they occur. Not only are the calls loud and monotonously repetitive, but they are carried on throughout the heat of the day when most birds are quiet. Together with a number of cuckoos, some Oriental barbets have been called brain-fever birds by those who have had to endure their interminable and monotonous calling. The metallic quality of the voices of several African and Oriental species has earned them names such as tinkerbird, blacksmith and coppersmith. FAMILY: Capitonidae, ORDER: Piciformes, CLASS: Aves. M.P.L.F.

BARBS, term loosely applied to certain members of the carp-like family Cyprinidae, referring to the small barbels round the mouth. Barbs include not only the genus *Barbus* but also the related genera *Hemi-*

barbus, Spinibarbus, Puntius and *Capoeta*. In Europe, the only barb is the barbel. Barbs are found throughout the temperate and tropical regions of the Old World and many of the smaller species are imported into Europe and the United States as aquarium fishes.

Barbs show a surprising range in size. The mahseer, the classic game fish of India, grows to about 9 ft (3 m) in length, while many aquarium barbs are fully grown at 3 in (7 cm). Identification of the species is often difficult, even for the specialist, because the shape and appearance of an individual often depend on the conditions in which it lives. In Africa, there are forms with thick, rubbery lips, forms with sharp, chisel-edged lips, and others with normal lips. Recent work has shown that the shape of the lips is in many, if not all, cases dependent on the nature of the lake or river bottom. Fishes living over rocks require a hard edge to the mouth to scrape off algae, while those with rubbery lips probably grub in the mud. There is also some evidence that lake dwellers are deeper-bodied than those that live in rivers.

Members of the Cyprinidae lack teeth in the jaws but are equipped with a set of teeth in the throat, the pharyngeal teeth. The number, size and shape of these reflect the diet of the fish and the degree to which the food must be chewed before swallowing. The pharyngeal teeth are a useful aid in identifying barbs, but this method is obviously of little help to the aquarist.

All the barbs lay eggs and many are quite easy to breed in an aquarium provided the parents are removed after they have scattered and fertilized the usually sticky eggs. Even the prettiest of barbs can become cannibals.

Most of the imported barbs come from India, Ceylon and the Indo-Malayan Archipelago. The commonest are the Rosy barb *Barbus concharius* from northern India; the Checkered barb *B. oligolepis* from Sumatra; the Black ruby *B. nigrofasciatus* from Ceylon; the Tiger barb *B. pentazona hexagona* from Sumatra; and the Two-spot barb *B. ficto* from Sumatra. The Golden barb, referred to as *'Barbus schuberti'*, is not a distinct species but seems to be a hybrid that suddenly appeared in aquaria in the United States and is closely related to a species from Singapore.

African barbs are less frequently imported but have been keenly studied because of their importance as food fishes in inland areas. An interesting species is the Blind barb *Caecobarbus geertsi* from the Congo. See Blind fishes. FAMILY: Cyprinidae, ORDER: Cypriniformes, CLASS: Pisces.

Golden barbs, of still waters of Central India.

BARBUDAS, of the genus *Polymixia*, these are small-scaled marine fishes found in both the Atlantic and Indo-Pacific regions at depths of about 600 ft (180 m). They grow to about 12 in (30 cm) in length, have two long barbels on the chin and are of little commercial importance. FAMILY: Polymixiidae, ORDER: Beryciformes, CLASS: Pisces.

BARK BEETLES, a name usually reserved for the *Engraver beetles but also used for other beetles that live under the bark of trees, such as members of the Flat bark beetles Cucujidae, the Cylindrical bark beetles Colydidae, the Comb-clawed bark beetles Alleculidae and the Melandryidae. Many of these beetles are predacious, feeding on other insects living beneath the bark, but some have forsaken this habit to become vegetarians and serious pests of stored grain. Examples of these pests are not uncommon among the Cucujidae, a family of 1,000 species. ORDER: Coleoptera, CLASS: Insecta, PHYLUM: Arthropoda.

BARKING DEER *Muntiacus muntjak*, name given to Indian muntjac because of its peculiar cry, like a hoarse resonant bark. See deer.

BARNACLES, crustaceans of the subclass Cirripedia. They are all marine and so very numerous that T. H. Withers, who published a monograph on them said: 'The present day may be truly regarded as the Age of Cirripedes, for they occur in countless millions on the shore-line of almost every coast, and are found attached to almost all

Two Tiger barbs *Barbus pentazona hexagona*, of Sumatra and Borneo, now to be found in aquaria in Europe and North America.

floating objects and to objects on the sea-bottom.' A mile-long stretch of rocky shore may have as many as 2,000 million Acorn barnacles. Like most crustaceans each individual animal goes through a series of juvenile stages before becoming an adult. Most barnacles have free-swimming larvae which pass through seven stages, six nauplius and a cypris stage, and in many places these form a notable part of the plankton at certain times of the year. Adult cirripedes are usually fixed to a solid support and they then look quite unlike other crustaceans, so much so that they used to be classified as Mollusca. Then, in 1829, J. Vaughan Thompson found the larvae, which were nauplii, like the larvae of crabs.

Cirripedia divides into a number of orders. The first of these, the Thoracica is made up of the suborders Pedunculata and Operculata. In the Pedunculata, the most primitive, the animal is enclosed in a number of calcareous plates and borne on a stalk or peduncle. The Pedunculata include the familiar barnacle often spoken of as the Ships' barnacle. Many pedunculate species, particularly those of the genus *Scalpellum*, live in deep water but *Pollicipes* is intertidal. On the exposed west coast of North America *Pollicipes polymerus* is a dominant component of the fauna covering vast areas of rock between tide-marks. The European species, *P. cornucopia* is considered by some as a gastronomic delicacy ('ponce-pied'). The genus *Lepas* (Goose barnacles) includes *L.*

Acorn barnacles coating a rock on the shore.

fasicularis, which constructs a float from the exuded cementing material which in other species serves to attach the animal firmly to the substratum. Other species of this genus are found attached to floating objects such as logs. This is the genus associated with the legend of the Barnacle geese.

The operculate or Acorn barnacles are common in the sublittoral and on all rocky coasts, often completely covering wide stretches of rock. They have no stalk and the calcareous plates have come together to form a chalky box containing the barnacle's body. The arrangement of the individual plates which make up this 'box' is important in classifying this section into its various genera. *Balanus,* Acorn barnacles, is a large and world-wide genus. *Coronula,* Whale barnacles, live attached to the skin of whales. Barnacles of other genera commonly settle on turtles. The genus *Tetraclita* is largely restricted to warm or warm-temperate waters.

Elminius, Catophragmus and *Octomeris* are genera of the southern hemisphere, but a species belonging to the first of these was carried to Britain on ships' hulls during World War II, is now common in Europe and in places has virtually displaced some indigenous species.

Three other groups must be briefly mentioned. The Acrothoracica are all small animals which live in cavities excavated in the shells of molluscs or the hard parts of coral. The Ascothoracica, again small, live at least partially embedded in various organisms, particularly corals and sponges. The Rhizocephala are totally parasitic on other crustaceans, an example being *Sacculina.

The Operculata or Acorn barnacles are all very similar in construction and in their life cycle. Attention is largely confined here to these. *Balanus balanoides,* the common European species, is typical. Its soft parts are enclosed in a shell cemented securely to the substratum. The shell, composed largely of calcium carbonate, is made up of a basis, which in some species, including *B. balanoides,* is not calcified, and the compartments forming the walls. Opposite the basis the shell opens to the exterior at the operculum which consists of four valves on a flexible membrane under the control of the animal inside and only when these are opened can the cirri be protruded and water flow in. The compartments forming the walls may, when seen in cross section, be simple solid structures or more complex, with tubes, variously orna-

Buoy-making barnacles, belonging to the Goose barnacles, make their own float. When young they settle on a piece of floating seaweed and as they grow they secrete a frothy jelly to support their own weight.

mented, running along their length and divided by transverse septa. During growth the opercular valves increase in size along their outer edges, the basis is added to around its circumference, so increasing its diameter, while the compartments increase in height at the base.

The body of the animal is attached underneath the opercular membrane round and beneath the large adductor muscle by which the two halves of the operculum are brought together. It consists of a thorax with a bag-like prosoma from which arise the cirri. The abdomen is vestigial. The mouth is situated on the prosoma. It should perhaps be emphasized that living tissue is continuous around the whole of the interior of the shell.

There are six pairs of cirri. Each cirrus arises from a two segmented support and bears two branches or rami. The five posterior pairs are homologous with the five pairs of walking legs in the higher crustaceans. The rami are articulated and bear spines. The support has muscles by which the cirri as a whole can be moved; the expansion or unrolling of the rami is brought about by hydrostatic pressure, and contraction by muscular action. The cirri are pushed out and then swept downwards acting as a drag-net to capture food and at the same time driving a current of water through the mantle cavity so bringing oxygen to the body surface through which it is absorbed. There are no gills as such but the branchiae, folded membranes of the internal surface of the mantle cavity, may aid respiratory exchange by increasing the surface area. The mouth leads to the oesophagus and thence to the gut which receives the hepatic caeca: the faeces are expelled at an anus which, because of the gut curvature, comes to be seated below the large sixth pair of cirri. There is no true heart; movements of the body drive the body fluids through various passages or lacunae surrounding the organs. The nervous system, like that of many crustaceans, is concentrated: there is a large supra-oesophageal ganglion connected by a pair of commissures to the infra-oesophageal ganglion and from these two ganglia nerves pass to all parts of the body.

With only one recently discovered exception the Operculata are all hermaphrodite, that is to say, both male and female reproductive organs are present in any individual. The testes are situated in the prosoma and spermatozoa are carried via the paired seminal vesicles to a penis which, particularly during the breeding season, is extremely long. During the breeding season the long penis can be protruded and inserted into a neighbouring barnacle which acts as a functional female. The early stages of the embryo are passed inside the parental body, at the base of the mantle cavity. Later, as larvae, they are expelled on the current of water induced by the movements of the cirri.

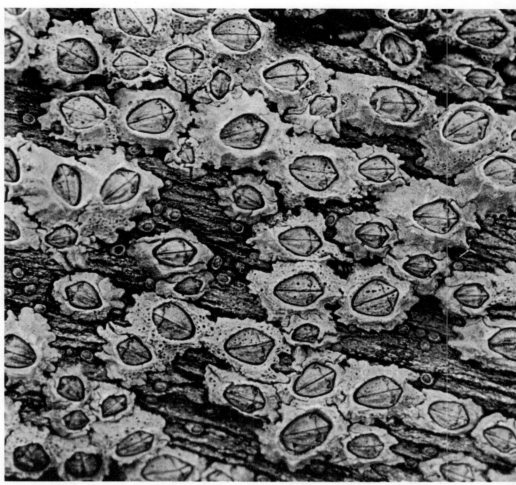

Acorn barnacles *Chthamalus stellatus*. The largest individuals may be ten years old.

Nauplii of Acorn barnacle *Balanus balanoides*, with diatoms in the marine plankton. Barnacles were thought to be Mollusca until their larvae were discovered, which showed them to be crustaceans.

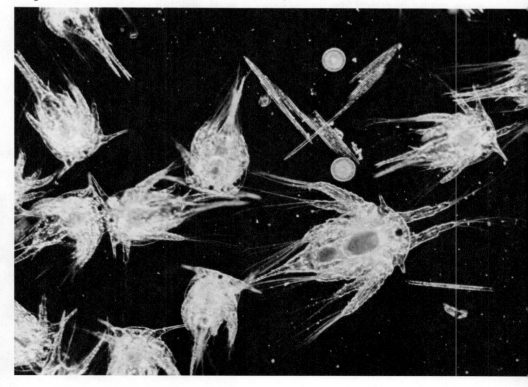

Goose barnacles, the common Ships' barnacles. An old legend told how they turned into geese.

The first stage of the nauplius larva does not feed but it soon moults to give the stage II nauplius which feeds on the micro-plankton. Further moults give rise to the remaining four nauplius stages and finally to the cypris larva. As the nauplius stages develop they increase in complexity and by stage VI the larva has paired compound eyes in addition to the single, median eye present from the first stage. The cypris larva is cigar-shaped, the body being enclosed within the two valve-like halves. It is a resting stage. When the cypris larva comes into contact with a solid surface it stops swimming and proceeds to explore the surface, 'walking' on its antennules, which have adhesive discs. The larva may leave the surface and swim away but if it does not then its movements become less marked and it eventually comes to rest attached by the antennules through which an adhesive cement is secreted. At this point begins the remarkable metamorphosis to the adult. The larva, in effect, stands on its head to change into the adult.

The extensive research in this century, in an attempt to find a way of preventing barnacles fouling ships' bottoms, has revealed what makes the larvae settle. A cypris larva, settling on a hard surface, 'explores' it. If barnacles have been living on it previously, or if there are barnacles still living on it, the cypris settles and changes to the adult. Otherwise it is likely to take off and continue swimming until it reaches another solid surface. SUBCLASS: Cirripedia, CLASS: Crustacea, PHYLUM: Arthropoda.   H.B.

BARNACLES. Mediaeval writers credited barnacles with a transformation more remarkable than that which we now know takes place from larva to adult. It was claimed that Barnacle geese arose from Goose barnacles. As Barnacle geese breed in the Arctic, beyond the mediaeval known world, and their nests were only discovered in 1891, some explanation was needed for their appearance each winter. It was generally agreed that the geese developed from stalked barnacles, which do indeed look like geese, their stalks looking like long necks and their shells resembling folded wings. The goose was supposed to develop within the shells and grow downwards suspended by its bill until mature. The origin of the barnacles was also explained by the early naturalists according to their individual fancies: that they arose either from froth or spume which hardened into shells, or from gummy excrescences on floating pine logs.

BARRACUDAS, tropical marine fishes related to the much more peaceable Grey mullets (family Mugilidae). The barracudas are fierce predators which, in some areas such as the West Indies, are more feared than sharks. The body is elongated and powerful, with two dorsal fins. The jaws are lined with sharp dagger-like teeth which make a neat, clean bite. There are many records of barracudas attacking divers and they appear to be attracted to anything that makes erratic movements or is highly coloured. They feed on fishes and have been seen to herd shoals of fish, rather after the manner of sheepdogs, until they are ready to attack.

The smallest of the barracuda *Sphyraena borealis* grows to about 18 in (46 cm) and is found along the North American Atlantic coast. The Great barracuda *Sphyraena barracuda* which grows to 8 ft (2·4 m) in length, is found in the western Pacific and on both sides of the tropical Atlantic. A certain mystery surrounds its habits, for it is known to attack divers in the West Indies but in the Pacific region, and particularly in Hawaii, it has the reputation of being harmless to man. The truth of this, however, has never been properly examined, since it is difficult to obtain accurate information from people who treat the fish with such great, and perhaps well advised, respect. In the Mediterranean there is a single species, *S. sphyraena,* which reaches 5 ft (1·5 m) in length.

Barracudas are good to eat and one Pacific species is regularly fished off the coast of California. In all, there are about a dozen species which are rather similar in appearance and habits but which rarely venture into temperate waters. FAMILY: Sphyraenidae, ORDER: Perciformes, CLASS: Pisces.

The Great barracuda *Sphyraena barracuda*, of both sides of the Atlantic, has a reputation for ferocity.

BARRACUDINAS, deep-sea fishes found in all oceans, belonging to the family Paralepididae, containing half a dozen genera. They are not related to the barracudas but are superficially similar although much smaller. The majority never exceed 2 ft (61 cm) length. Their slender bodies are in many cases scaleless, except for the lateral line and in some species a luminous duct is present along the underside of the stomach although the genus *Paralepis* contains species with scaly bodies. *Lestidium ringens* is found at depths down to 1500 ft (500 m) off the American Pacific coast. Like most barracudinas, it grows to 8 in (20 cm) long and is a fish eater. Like many deep-sea fishes barracudinas make considerable vertical migrations at night, some species in the south Pacific coming so close to the surface that fishermen attract them to lights to catch them. A large part of our knowledge of these fishes comes from specimens spat up by tunas caught in deep water. FAMILY: Paralepididae, ORDER: Salmoniformes, CLASS: Pisces.

BARRELFISH, one of the several common names applied to butterfishes or stromateids. The barrelfish *Hyperoglyphe perciforma* is also called the logfish, rudderfish or Black rudderfish. *Schedophilus medusophagus,* sometimes known as the portrush or Portuguese barrelfish, has now been identified as the young of *Centrolophus britannicus* (see blackfish). The former is an Atlantic fish found along both American and European coasts, with occasional British records. It has a compressed, fairly deep body of a general purplish-black colour and is distinguished from the second species by the presence of a series of unconnected spines in front of the dorsal fin. Like all stromateids, these fishes have a muscular oesophagus armed with ridges or teeth. The name barrelfish derives from this fish's habit of accompanying floating objects and often entering boxes or barrels; logfish refers to individuals found swimming near barnacle covered logs. *Schedophilus perciformis* feeds on barnacles while *S. medusophagus,* as its name implies, feeds largely on jellyfishes. FAMILY: Stromateidae, ORDER: Perciformes, CLASS: Pisces.

BARRIERS, the factors which restrict the spread of animals. Most animals can tolerate only a limited range of variation in the physical characteristics of their environment. These characteristics include the temperature, the relative humidity of air, the salinity of water and the concentrations of oxygen and carbon dioxide. Areas where these physical characteristics differ from those tolerated or preferred by an animal therefore represent obstacles to its distribution. Where it is completely intolerable to a particular

animal, the resulting barrier may be absolute, the animal being unable to cross it. As far as marine animals are concerned, wide stretches of land are an absolute barrier, as is the ocean to many freshwater fish and land animals. Stretches of ocean are the main barriers which separate the terrestrial faunas of the different continents; the resulting differences between these faunas make it possible to distinguish these as separate zoogeographical regions.

Over the long periods of geological time, chance events may result in the passage of an animal across even an apparently absolute barrier. For example, many amphibians have colonized the scattered Pacific islands, crossing wide stretches of sea in which they cannot survive. These crossings have presumably been made in masses of floating vegetation, such as are swept down rivers after torrential rains. Such a rare, haphazard crossing of a barrier against all apparent odds is sometimes known as 'sweepstakes colonization'.

Within a continent, climatic differences are the basis of most barriers. For example, it is noticeable that there is a progressive reduction in the variety of animals present as the cold arctic or antarctic latitudes are approached. The extent to which different groups of animals can colonize these inhospitable regions varies. Birds and mammals, insulated by their feathers or hair, are more successful in this than are other vertebrates. In the far north, many of the birds and mammals can exist only as seasonal migrants, retiring southwards at the end of the summer when the climate becomes much more severe and the food supply is consequently diminished.

The arctic and antarctic regions act as fringes to the habitable regions of the world. In contrast, the climates of such features as high mountain chains or deserts form barriers lying between more hospitable areas. Animals which can survive for a relatively short time in such environments can therefore cross these barriers. Since these barriers are in this way selective in their action, allowing some animals to pass but not others, they are sometimes referred to as filters. The Sahara and Gobi deserts and the Himalayan Mountains are the filter barriers which separate the tropical Ethiopian and Oriental zoogeographic regions from the rest of the Old World. Other filters may be less extreme in their climate; the cool Mexican uplands have acted as a filter between the faunas of North and South America, animals which require a tropical climate being unable to pass through into North America. The Bering region has also acted as a filter, between North America and Asia. It was more important as a colonization route earlier in the Tertiary when its climate was warmer and the Bering Strait was narrower

or even absent, the two continents being joined by a land bridge.   C.B.C.

BASILISKS, lizards of the genus *Basiliscus* containing several species inhabiting Central America and ranging as far north as central Mexico. They live along the banks of the smaller rivers or streams where they bask during the day or sleep at night on bushes that overhang the water. Basilisks are slender lizards with long slim toes and tail and the males are often adorned with crests.

The basilisk, South American reptile, named after the legendary monster of Europe, best known for its running on water.

Speed is the chief means of snatching up food (insects and small rodents or birds) and escaping enemies. When attempting to escape basilisks head for water and run across it. A fringe of scales along the lengthy rear toes provides support as they dash over the surface. Basilisks are known as teteterecha in some parts of their range as this resembles the sound they make when running on water. Another name is the Jesus Cristo lizard for the ability to 'walk on the water'. As its speed slackens, however, the lizard begins to sink and must swim in conventional manner like any other lizard.

Most colourful and largest of the basilisks is the rare Green crested basilisk *Basiliscus plumbifrons* of Costa Rica. The male has a large, ornamental crest on its head, another along its back and one on the tail, the use of which is not fully known unless it is used to threaten other males.

Basilisks hatch from $\frac{1}{2}-\frac{3}{4}$ in (c. 2 cm), nearly round eggs that may be white or brown and are buried by the female in damp sand near stream banks. Hatching takes 18–30 days (normally 20–24 days) and the tiny youngsters are replicas of the adults except they have no crests. Basilisks are normally some shade of brown with white or yellow bands or mottling. In the Green basilisks, the young are brown with only a trace of greenish tint to the lighter markings on neck and sides. They turn green after approaching $\frac{1}{3}$ of the adult size, and the males begin rapidly developing a crest when $\frac{2}{3}$ grown.

In the Banded basilisk *Basiliscus vittatus,* the colouration is variable. It is dark brown in the daytime, but when resting at night on branches over streams, the lateral bands are vivid yellow or white. In captivity, the basilisk seems to lose its ability to undergo such drastic colour change between night and day. No such colour change ability has been noted in captivity with the Green basilisk, and it appears to be a vivid green at all times. FAMILY: Iguanidae, ORDER: Squamata, CLASS: Reptilia.   R.P.

BASILISK, also known as the cockatrice, is a legendary animal and was once regarded as the king of serpents. It had the body of a barnyard cockerel and the tail of a serpent and even its glance was said to be fatal. One remedy indulged in for clearing the land of basilisks was for a man to clothe himself in an armour of mirrors. Any basilisk he met would see its own image in the mirrors and would be killed. A basilisk was said to be the offspring of a mating between a cockerel and a snake, the egg being watched over by a toad. In the Dark Ages a toad found squatting near an egg at Basle in Switzerland was solemnly tried and publicly burned at the stake on suspicion of being implicated in the birth of a basilisk.

It is highly likely that the whole legend hinges on the well-known phenomenon of a barnyard hen changing her sex as she ages, crowing and growing wattles, but still laying eggs.

BASKET STARS, brittlestars in which the simple five-armed symmetry is obscured by the numerous side branches of the arms. Up to 2 ft (61 cm) across the spread arms they are found in deep seas down to 5,000 ft (1,600 m). The curling tendril-like branches of the arms recall the Gorgon's head of Greek mythology. When feeding a Basket star clings to a rock with two arms and holds the others up, like a basket, to catch food. See brittlestars. ORDER: Euryalae, CLASS: Ophiuroidea, PHYLUM: Echinodermata.

BASKING SHARK *Cetorhinus maximus,* second only to the Whale shark in size and immediately recognizable by its very long gill clefts which extend from the upper to the

lower surface of the body. There are two dorsal fins and one anal fin, very small teeth in the jaws, and the general body colour is a grey-brown. The maximum size of these sharks is usually given as 45 ft (13·5 m) and certainly fishes of 30 ft (9 m) are not uncommon. Unlike most of its relatives, the Basking shark is not carnivorous but feeds by straining plankton from the water. The gill arches are equipped with rows of fine rakers (up to 4 in/10 cm long and over 1,000 in each row) and these form a fine sieve through which the water is strained before leaving by the gill clefts. This system is clearly an efficient one since it can provide enough food for an animal that may weigh over 4 tons (4,000 kg). Basking sharks lacking gillrakers are sometimes found and it is thought that the rakers may be shed in winter and regrown every spring. They derive their name from their habit of lying at the surface. They are not dangerous to man, except perhaps accidentally when in collision with small boats.

The Basking shark is the only member of its family and appears to be found everywhere, but chiefly in temperate waters. It is fished commercially off the western coasts of Ireland (where they are known as muldoans) and Scotland, as well as off the coasts of New England, California, Peru and Ecuador. The fishes are mainly caught by harpoon as they 'bask' at the surface. The flesh is less important than the oils from the liver, which are used in tanning processes. The liver itself may comprise a tenth of the total weight of the fish and it is the buoyancy this affords that enables the Basking shark to lie motionless at the surface. Little is known about its breeding but a Basking shark off Norway in 1923 immediately gave birth to six live

young when hooked. FAMILY: Cetorhinidae, ORDER: Pleurotremata, CLASS: Chondrichthyes.

BASKING SHARK MONSTER. The cast-up carcases of large marine animals, such as whales and sharks, have sometimes aroused extraordinary interest and speculation because decomposition and battering by the waves has altered their shape beyond recognition and led to their being described as sea-serpents. The most famous carcase is the 'Stronsay monster' cast up in 1808 on the shores of Stronsay, one of the Orkney Islands to the north of Scotland. Detailed descriptions made by several men tallied quite closely. The 'monster' was about 55 ft (14·5 m) long and appeared to have a long neck and tail, a small head and strangest of all, three pairs of limbs. The skull, some vertebrae and a few other pieces were removed and preserved before the carcase broke up and was washed away. From this evidence Patrick Neill, a Scottish naturalist, was able to describe a species new to science: *Halsydrus pontopiddani,* named after Pontopiddan who described a 'sea-orm' in his *Natural History of Norway.* Later, however, the copies of the eye witnesses' reports came into the hands of a London surgeon who was studying the anatomy of the Basking shark. His suspicions were aroused by many of the details and on examining the preserved vertebrae he was able to pronounce that the Stronsay monster was no more than the remains of a large Basking shark. The narrow neck and tail were formed by the rotting away of the lower jaw and tail fin and the three pairs of legs were the two sets of paired fins and the claspers.

Bass of the coastal seas of northwest Europe, excellent angling fishes.

BASS, a term used in Europe for the Sea perch *Dicentrarchus labrax* and its close relative the Black-spotted bass *D. punctatus* (both erroneously placed in the genus *Morone* in the older literature). The bass is considered by many to be one of the best of European angling fishes. It is a coastal fish that often enters estuaries and even ascends rivers. It is found in the Mediterranean and off the coasts of Spain and Portugal but reaches the southern coasts of the British Isles. It is found off shelving sand or shingle beaches and is often fished for in the breakers, where it feeds on fishes (sandeels, sprat and herring). Specimens of 18 lb (8 kg) have been caught but fishes of 2–7 lb (0·9–3 kg) are more usual. There are two dorsal fins, the first spiny and separated from the second. The back is blue-green, the flanks silver with a black lateral line and a white belly. This fish is considered excellent eating. The Black-spotted bass is a smaller fish, reaching 2 ft (60 cm) in length and the body is speckled with black spots. This species does not reach as far north as the British Isles. See also Black bass. FAMILY: Serranidae, ORDER: Perciformes, CLASS: Pisces.

BATESON W., 1861–1926. British founder of the science of genetics, originator of the word itself, and occupant of the first Chair of Genetics in Cambridge, England. He confirmed Mendel's re-discovered work on inheritance, and supported his principle of the transmission of characters by definite entities—later called genes. Following studies in Europe, Asia and the USA, he published in 1894 his classic *Materials for the Study of Variation,* stressing the discontinuities in heredity. He was reluctant to accept the connexion between genes and chromosomes but eventually (1922) capitulated on this point.

BATFISHES, a common name given to two rather different groups of fishes. Members of the family Ogcocephalidae, a family of the anglerfishes, are sometimes referred to as batfishes although the term is more appropriately used for members of the Platacidae, a family containing marine perch-like fishes with greatly extended wing-like dorsal and anal fins. Species of *Platax* have highly compressed, almost circular bodies and their long fins give them a bat-like appearance when swimming. They grow to about 2 ft (60 cm) and are found in the Indo-Pacific region. They are beautiful fishes with red-yellow colouring, and dark vertical bands in the young which disappear with age. Such colouring would seem to make them more conspicuous but in fact these fishes strongly resemble floating and yellowing leaves of the Red mangrove. When chased by a predator in a mangrove swamp, the fishes stop swimming and drift motionless like leaves. They

The batfish *Platax*, one of several kinds of remarkable fishes that have winglike fins.

feed on small crustaceans and the general detritus of coastal and mangrove swamp areas. FAMILY: Platacidae, ORDER: Perciformes, CLASS: Pisces.

BATH SPONGE, the fibrous skeleton of an animal used since time immemorial for a variety of purposes, not only for bathing but in a wide range of commercial purposes. In life the skeleton, composed of spongin, a substance related to *chitin, is covered with a yellow flesh bounded externally by a purplish-black skin which may be pale yellow when the sponge has been growing in dim light. The Bath, or Commercial, sponge lives in warm seas, from shallow waters to not more than 600 ft (200 m) and may be one of a few species, the chief of which are *Spongia officinalis,* with a fine-meshed skeleton, and *Hippospongia equina,* with a coarser skeleton. The main centres of sponge fisheries are the Mediterranean, especially the eastern half, and the Gulf of Mexico and Caribbean Sea, especially around the Bahamas, Florida and Honduras. Bath sponges also occur, but in more limited numbers, in the Red Sea, Indian Ocean and on the Great Barrier Reef

of Australia. FAMILY: Spongidae, ORDER: Demospongiae, CLASS: Gelatinosa, PHYLUM: Parazoa.

BATRACHIA, an obsolete name for the Amphibia.

BATS, one of the most distinctive groups of animals. They are mammals since they are covered by fur and suckle their young, yet they can all fly in a sustained manner which no other mammal can do. They therefore form a well-defined division called the Order Chiroptera, a name meaning 'hand-wings'. Because all bats are nocturnal in habits, and the majority are tropical in distribution, they are relatively little known and it is seldom realized that they are both numerous and diverse, with about 800 species or about one-seventh of all mammals.

The bats belong to the basically primitive group of mammals called the Unguiculata which also includes the primates and the insectivores. Bats are probably descended from insectivores but their origins are rather obscure because they have left few fossils. The earliest known bats, from the Eocene period, are remarkably similar to present day forms. It is therefore impossible to tell how flight developed or what bats were like before they could fly. Linnaeus first classified bats with primates because their forelimbs bear 'hands' instead of paws and because the males have a free penis. These similarities now seem rather superficial, but there is little doubt that the two groups are quite closely related.

The order is subdivided into two sub-orders—the Megachiroptera and the Microchiroptera. Although these names literally mean 'big bats' and 'small bats', there is a considerable overlap in their size ranges. The Megachiroptera vary in weight from about 1 oz (25–30 g) to 2 lb (900 g) with wingspans of 10 in (25 cm) to over 5 ft (150 cm), while adult Microchiroptera range from about $\frac{1}{8}$ oz (3·5 g) to $6\frac{1}{2}$ oz (180 g) with wingspans of 6 in (15 cm) to 3 ft (90 cm). The most obvious physical distinctions are that Megachiroptera have very large eyes and nearly always have a claw on the first finger as well as on the thumb. Because most of them have dog-like faces they are often called 'flying foxes'. The much more diverse Microchiroptera are divided further into four superfamilies and 16 families; they show variable development of the eyes, a wide variety of faces many of which are bizarre at first sight, and they never have a claw on the fingers. A summary of the classification and the characteristics of each family is given in the table.

Because bats are little known, especially to the layman, very few of them have common names other than simple adjectives that are often ambiguous and confusing. Thus the Megachiroptera are often called 'fruit bats' but not all eat fruit; the Microchiroptera are often called 'insectivorous bats' although their diets vary tremendously and some eat fruit. Again the same name has been given to unrelated bats: for example, three different families are called 'tomb bats' although none lives exclusively in tombs; 'false vampires' is applied to the Megadermatidae and to the Phyllostomatidae, and 'free-tailed bats' include the primitive Emballonuridae and the advanced Molossidae but apparently not the Rhinopomatidae whose tails are much freer. Finally the largest family, the Vespertilionidae, has no commonly accepted name although they are sometimes rather lamely called 'vesper bats' or inaccurately 'common bats'. With few exceptions, therefore, it is safer to use the formal scientific names for all bats and the table may be used for reference to these.

The body form of bats is largely governed by the exacting requirements of flight. In this respect all bats have much in common and they have solved the problems of flight in quite different ways from birds. In general the skeleton is frail and light but the fore-limbs are enormously developed. The upper arm is fairly short and strong with a powerful shoulder joint to bear the weight of the body. In the so-called advanced families each arm has a double articulation with the shoulder blade, making a firm hinge for flapping movements. The forearm is very long with only a single bone, the radius, and bears a short, compact wrist in which many of the bones are fused together for further strength. From this projects a short thumb with a claw used for climbing or walking. In vampires which are especially agile on the ground, the thumb is well developed as a 'foot' and bears a fleshy pad that acts as a 'sole'. The fingers are all very long with extended shanks between the knuckles; the index and middle fingers are close together at the leading edge of the wing while the ring and little fingers fan out behind to support the main wing surface. This whole arrangement gives fine control of the wing shape since all the joints can be flexed by tendons operated from muscles in the arm. Thus bats are by far the most manoeuvrable of aerial animals.

The whole of the forearm is webbed by a thin, double layer of skin which forms the wing membrane. This runs from the shoulder across the kink of the elbow to the wrist, between all the fingers (but rarely includes the thumb) and from the little finger backwards along the body to the ankle of the back leg. It contains elastic strands and fine muscle fibres within it so that it collapses when the wing is folded and does not interfere with walking. In flight it also acts as a radiator since it contains a network of fine blood vessels in which the blood is cooled to prevent the bat becoming overheated by its exertions. When the bat lands the blood supply to the wings is much reduced so that heat is then conserved.

The back legs of bats have thighs and shins of roughly equal length and a short, round foot with five small toes bearing sharp claws. The tendons in the foot prevent the toes from straightening when the leg is extended so that bats can hang from a toe-hold without effort and indeed often die without falling off. The hips are also unusual because the joints are permanently twisted so that the

The pipistrelle *Pipistrellus pipistrellus* in flight. Flash photographs in sequence show the action of the wings, legs and tail (top and centre). A series of flash photographs shows the action of the Greater horseshoe bat *Rhinolophus ferrumequinum* as it flies across the field of view (bottom).

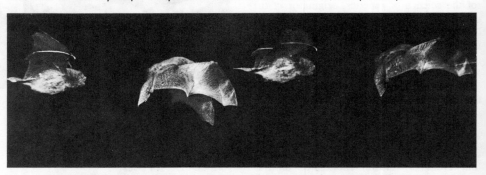

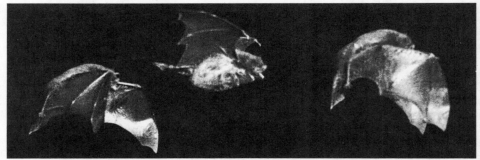

knees point upwards over the back instead of forwards. This position is the most convenient for hanging and squirrels hold their legs this way when descending trees head first. In bats it also allows the legs to kick downwards to assist the wingbeat when flying.

The tail and the flight membrane between the legs are very variable and are a distinguishing feature of most families. The Megachiroptera have at most a simple flap along the inside leg and the feet are held together in flight; the tail if present is short and free. In the Microchiroptera there is generally, but not always, a large tail membrane stretched between the legs, with the actual tail incorporated in it to various degrees: running to the edge or beyond it, emerging from the upper surface of the membrane before reaching the free edge, or being completely absent so that the membrane is unsupported down the middle. In all cases, however, the trailing edge of the tail membrane is strengthened by a whip-like cartilage called the calcar which projects towards the mid-line from the ankle.

In general the bats are a tropical group and there show their greatest diversity. Any warm, forested region might have over 100 species from as many as nine families, thus comprising an important part of the fauna. In temperate regions the numbers of individuals, species and families decline rapidly as the climate gets colder. The south of England has 14 species of two families but Scotland has only six species, all from one family, the Vespertilionidae. Only two other families penetrate into the southern tips of Europe with one species each, and there are 31 European species altogether.

Three families of bats are found throughout the tropics; the rest are restricted to the Old World (eight families) or the New World (six families) although some of them are very local. The main limitation to distribution appears to be the dependability of food sources (all the bats of temperate regions are insectivorous and hibernate in winter when insects are scarce). Flight confers great mobility compared with terrestrial mammals, and bats are often found on isolated islands if conditions are suitable. For example, there are two species on the Galapagos Islands and two more in New Zealand, which has no other indigenous mammals. Some genera, such as the mouse-eared bats *Myotis* of the Vespertilionidae, are very widespread indeed and one species has successfully invaded Britain in the last few years.

The breeding of bats is as unusual as their other characteristics. Being placental mammals they have internal fertilization, nurture the foetus in the womb and give birth to well developed young, usually singly, although twins are quite common in some species. Mating occurs in the daytime roost

A False vampire *Cardioderma cor*, showing extensive development of the ears.

and courtship appears to be perfunctory. Promiscuity is the rule and both pair formation and paternal care are unknown. In temperate climates the breeding cycle of Microchiroptera is interrupted by hibernation since mating occurs in the autumn. The sperm are then stored inside the female until ovulation, and fertilization occurs after she awakens in the spring. Although further matings may occur in the spring, it seems certain that delayed fertilization is responsible for the majority of conceptions. The young are born in all-female nursing colonies within a period of a few days during early summer. The mothers have two functional teats on the sides of the chest, but some bats also have a second, non-lactating pair in the groin which the baby holds during flight. When the baby grows too heavy to be carried it is left behind in the colony while the mother is hunting. Its limb bones rapidly grow to almost full length, long before the adult weight is achieved. This may be important for the first flight is often critical. Bat roosts are generally inaccessible from the ground and a failure to fly competently the first time would nearly always be fatal.

Tropical bats that live under constant climatic conditions appear to breed repeatedly throughout the year. Female Molossidae are sometimes pregnant while still suckling a baby, and a young female bat may itself become pregnant before it is fully

weaned. In other regions the birth of bats occurs at the onset of the rainy season and weaning coincides with the period of greatest food abundance. In at least one species of the Megachiroptera the egg is fertilized after mating, as is usual in mammals, but there is then a delay of some months before it becomes implanted in the womb and begins to develop.

One of the most striking features of bats as a group is the wide range of their dietary specializations. In the Old World the Megachiroptera are completely vegetarian, mostly eating fruit, flowers or pollen. One small group in the Far East, with an isolated member in Africa, are almost exclusively nectar drinkers. They hover or perch close to night-opening flowers and sip the rich fluid with very long, rough-tipped tongues. This habit is so well established that these bats have almost lost their teeth, while certain trees have become specialized for being pollinated by their visits. The majority of the Old World Microchiroptera are insectivorous but a few, notably the Megadermatidae, are 'bats of prey', hunting small vertebrate animals such as mice, lizards and other bats. One or two species in Asia probably catch small fish with their back feet as they fly low over open water.

In the New World, where the Megachiroptera do not exist, the Microchiroptera show the full range of their evolutionary possibilities. Again most families are insectivorous but the large family Phyllostomatidae also includes specialized fruit-eaters, nectar-drinkers, powerful bats of prey and some species that eat any of these foods. The closely related true vampires feed only on the blood of larger vertebrates, specializing either on birds or on mammals which are attacked as they sleep. Not surprisingly vampire bats possess a number of unusual adaptations for this mode of life; they have large, sharp incisor teeth to open a wound gently, a muscular, grooved tongue for sipping the blood and secretions in their saliva which prevent the blood from clotting. They can imbibe enormous quantities of blood and excrete the excess water rapidly, and are very agile on the ground in case their host should awaken when they are so engorged that they fly only with difficulty.

Finally there are two specialized New World fishing bats, one in the Noctilionidae and a Mexican member of the Vespertilionidae. Both have very large back feet which seize fish from the water during flight. Most bats appear to obtain the water they need either from their food or by drinking from standing water as they fly very low over the surface. Open freshwater is also a good source of insects, some emerging from metamorphosis and others trapped accidentally by surface tension. It may well be that fishing originally developed from the habit of

Micropteropus pusillus, Pteropidae.

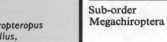

Hypsignathus manstrosus (male), Pteropidae.

Eidolon helvum, Pteropidae.

Rhinopoma hardwickei, Rhinopomatidae.

Taphozous hildegardeae, Emballonuridae.

Noctilio leporinus, Noctilionidae.

Nycteris arge, Nycteridae.

Lavia frons, Megadermatidae.

  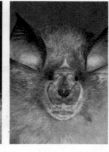 

Rhinolophus landeri, Rhinolophidae.

Triaenops afer, Hipposideridae.

	Family name	Some common synonyms	Ap... sp...
Sub-order Megachiroptera	Pteropidae	Fruit-bats, flying foxes	
Sub-order Microchiroptera — Superfamily Emballonuroidea (primitive simple nosed bats)	Rhinopomatidae	Mouse-tailed bats, tomb bats	
	Emballonuridae	Tomb bats, free-tailed bats, sheath-tailed bats, sac-winged bats, reflex-winged bats	
	Noctilionidae	Bull-dog bats, fishing bats	
Superfamily Rhinolophoidea (Old World leaf-nosed bats)	Nycteridae	Slit-faced bats, hollow faced bats	
	Megadermatidae	False vampires	
	Rhinolophidae	Horseshoe bats	
	Hipposideridae	Horseshoe bats, leaf-nosed bats	
Superfamily Phyllostomatoidea (New World leaf-nosed bats)	Phyllostomatidae	Leaf-nosed bats, spear-nosed bats, false vampires	
	Desmodontidae	Vampires	
Superfamily Vespertilionoidea (advanced simple nosed bats)	Natalidae	Funnel-eared bats, long-legged bats	
	Furipteridae	Thumbless bats, smoky bats	
	Thyropteridae	Sucker-footed bats, disc-winged bats	
	Myzopodidae	Sucker-footed bats, disc-winged bats	
	Vespertilionidae	Common bats, vesper bats, typical bats	
	Mystacinidae	Short-tailed bats	
	Molossidae	Free-tailed bats, mastiff bats, tomb bats	

...guishing features; roosting position	Distribution	Diet	Echolocation notes
...arge eyes, claw on 1st finger, tail plays ...ve part in flight; hang free, generally ...open.	Old World tropics	Fruit, flowers, nectar, pollen	Only found in *Rousettus* which clicks its tongue
...ong, thin free tail, tragus in ear, nose ...eshy pad to close nostrils: hangs from	Africa to India	Insects	Complex sweeps from the mouth
...large eyes; short tail free above the ...ane, pouches in the wings quite com-...ips doubly folded; hang from walls.	World-wide tropics	Insects	Complex sweeps from the mouth
...idely separated on head, deep jowls, ...canine teeth, long legs with large feet, ...ail free above membrane; hang from	Caribbean, Central and S. America	Insects, fish	Sweeps and constant notes from the mouth
...inute, large ears, nostrils in a slit with ...pads either side, tail very long, in ...ane with T-shaped tip; hang free.	Africa, one in Far East	Insects	Complex sweeps from the nostrils
...ears joined together; large eyes and ...af, large membrane between legs but ...; hang free.	Old World tropics	Insects, vertebrate prey	Complex sweeps from the nostrils
...mall, mobile independent ears, no ...elaborate nose-leaf with 'spear' above, ...ds over back; hang free.	Old World including Britain	Insects	Pure constant note with terminal sweeps from nostrils, synchronized to ear movements
...Rhinolophidae but nose-leaf has a ...t bar above or a trident structure; ...hang free.	Old World tropics	Insects	(see above)
...independent ears with tragus, simple ...nose-leaf, very variable tail but often ...ove membrane; variable posture.	U.S.A. to S. America	Insects, vertebrate prey, fruit, pollen, nectar	Few constant notes from mouth, mainly complex sweeps from the nostrils
...fleshy nose-leaf, muscular legs, large ...with pad, large incisor teeth, tail free ...membrane; hang from walls.	Central and S. America	Vertebrate blood	Complex sweeps from the nostrils
...eyes, large ears encircle face, long ...ery long limbs and flight membrane ...orating tail; hang free.	Caribbean, S. America	Insects	Pure sweeps from the mouth
...ears, minute thumb, tail in membrane ...es not reach edge; posture unknown.	Caribbean, Central and S. America	Insects	Unknown
...r suckers on wrists and ankles; tail ...s slightly beyond membrane; cling ...olled banana leaves.	Caribbean	Insects	Unknown
...r suckers on wrists and ankles, ears ...ith unique lobe at base, tail projects ...yond membrane; cling to leaves?	Madagascar	Insects	Unknown
...ears with tragus, tail in membrane ...e, very variable appearance; hang on ...r in crevices, rarely free.	World-wide, including Britain	Insects, rarely fish or vertebrate prey	Pure sweeps from the mouth; some give pure notes when flying high
...leathery, rolled up at rest, pointed ears ...ng tragus, tail free above membrane; ...n walls.	New Zealand	Insects	Unknown
...fixed ears, wrinkled, heavy jowls, ...ar tail beyond membrane which slides ...walls, crevices, rarely free.	World-wide if warm	Insects	Slow sweeps or almost constant notes from mouth

Chilonycteris rubiginosa, Phyllostomatidae.

Carollia perspicillata, Phyllostomatidae.

Diaemus youngi, Desmodontidae.

Natalus tumidirostris, Natalidae.

Scotophilus nigrita, Vespertilionidae.

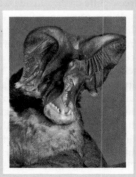

Otomops martiensseni, Molossidae.

catching insects in such situations. As the bats became more adept at catching fish they were then able to exploit the sea as well as inland waters.

A word should be said about bats in captivity. It may be supposed that any bat would form an unusual and fascinating pet, but they are difficult to keep and may even form a health hazard. Many Megachiroptera keep fit and healthy on fruit such as bananas with added vitamins. They may become quite tame but are rather messy and smelly for a domestic environment. The larger ones need a great deal of space to fly successfully and this should not be attempted in ordinary rooms. Most of the Microchiroptera have such highly specialized requirements that they are very difficult to maintain adequately. Moreover in many parts of the world they may be infected with dangerous diseases such as rabies and great care should be taken when handling them as a bite may prove fatal.

No bats make nests or any other form of home for themselves. Even when rearing their young they merely select an existing site as a suitable roost. The only modifications to the roost are made by certain fruit-eaters in the Phyllostomatidae which hang under palm leaves. These bats are said to bite through the main ribs of a row of fronds so that they hang down and form a V-roof for concealment and protection. Other bats roost in a wide variety of situations, singly, in small groups or in colonies which may include many thousands or even millions of animals. Caves of course are very commonly occupied by bat colonies, for they offer equable conditions and freedom from disturbance. But caves are unevenly distributed and some obligate cave-dwelling species are widely scattered, although each colony may contain enormous numbers of bats. Less demanding species inhabit buildings, hollow trees, culverts and even the spaces between boulders. Some Microchiroptera cling to the inside of young, rolled leaves of the banana family and some squeeze through thin cracks to occupy the hollow sections of bamboo stems. Other bats, including most of the Megachiroptera, roost out in the open on trees, cliffs or the outside walls of buildings.

When roosting, different bats adopt one of three different postures. Many hang free from branches or irregularities of horizontal 'ceilings' and wrap their wings around themselves, one over the other. Most of these bats appear to be unable to walk on the ground and although some of them may land to feed, they can only escape again by spreading their wings and 'flipping' themselves into the air. Others hang from vertical surfaces with the wings folded on either side of the body. The thumbs may then obtain additional purchase and the arms are sometimes used as props to hold the head well out from the

Fruit bats *Pteropus rufus maaagasariensis* roosting in a tree. At dusk they fly off in search of fruiting trees, to gorge themselves on the fruit.

wall. On the ground such bats can run about quite quickly on their wrists and back feet. Finally, some bats try to touch a solid surface with their backs and squeeze themselves into protective crevices, generally entering backwards. There appears to be a natural correlation between the exposure of the roost and the degree of alertness during rest. Crevice-seeking bats and some from deep caves may sleep very deeply, becoming active only slowly when disturbed, whereas most bats in exposed positions are able to take flight immediately when approached and often appear to have good vision although their eyes may not be large.

The nature of the roost also influences the colours of bats. Those species that sleep in the open are usually drab in colour and inconspicuous when resting. Many have bold dark and light patterns, patches or stripes on their bodies, head or wings which act as disruptive colouration. Cave-living bats experience almost perpetual darkness so that

colour is of little consequence. Patterning is rarely seen and most species are drab but many have two colour phases; some individuals are brown while others have brightly coloured fur, usually red, orange or bright yellow. One brightly coloured bat roosts in acacia-thorn bushes in open country. This is *Lavia,* an African member of the Megadermatidae. Its fur is long and grey but its wings, ears and nose-leaf are bright yellow or orange. This colour may protect it from overheating when exposed to bright sunlight, but it also makes the bats almost indistinguishable from dead leaves and seed pods.

Mammals are typically warm-blooded and the larger Megachiroptera maintain their temperature constant in the characteristic way. But during daily sleep many Microchiroptera allow their body temperatures to fall to only a little above that of the surrounding air. Similarly hummingbirds also allow their temperatures to fall during rest at night. This may be necessary to conserve food supplies over the daily period of en-forced fasting. Small warm-blooded animals must spend much metabolic energy in keep-ing warm because they have a relatively large area of body surface for their weight. Thus shrews, which are of comparable size, maintain a constant body temperature but must be active and feed regularly throughout both day and night; they also die of old age in a year or two whereas small bats in temperate regions may live to be over twenty. The bats may sleep in deep caves where there is little or no distinction between day and night, yet they awaken at the correct time each evening by means of internal physiological 'clocks' in the brain. They shiver violently for some minutes in order to warm themselves before taking flight to emerge and feed in the open air.

During the winter in temperate countries the food of bats becomes scarce. Unlike small insectivorous birds, bats seldom migrate for long distances. Instead most of them hibernate. During the autumn they become very fat with accumulated food reserves and sink into a dormant state that is more extreme than daily sleep. Heart-rate, breathing and all other bodily functions are greatly suppressed throughout the winter. The external conditions during hibernation are quite critical and some bats fly long distances to reach suitable caves before winter. The temperature must be low or the metabolism will be too rapid and food reserves will be exhausted too soon, but it must not be too low or the bats will die of cold. About $39-50°F$ ($4-10°C$) is a suitable range. Bats must also conserve water during hibernation. Although breathing is very slow there will be a steady loss by evaporation in the lungs unless the external humidity is high. The conditions selected by the bats are sometimes so damp that dew forms on their fur as they sleep.

It is not true, however, that hibernation is uninterrupted, for bats are sometimes seen flying about in mid-winter. Bats marked with identification rings in the wild are often found to have moved between observations and may even fly some miles from one hibernation cave to another. Experimenters have monitored the body temperatures of bats kept in refrigerators and have shown that even under very constant environmental conditions the bats waken spontaneously from time to time.

Almost every aspect of bat biology is influenced by the fact that they are nocturnal animals. There really are no exceptions to this rule, although some species become active well before sunset, especially in shady forests, and a few sometimes make short flights during the day. Two reasons can be suggested for this exclusiveness. First their method of radiative cooling from the naked wings would be disadvantageous in sunlight,

when heat would be absorbed rather than lost; birds have avoided this problem by using evaporative cooling with a unique pattern of air-flow in their lungs. Secondly the bats possess well developed sensory systems for flight guidance at night and are thus able to avoid competition from the predominantly diurnal birds.

The Megachiroptera all possess very large eyes, capable of superb night vision, al-though they are of course unable to see in complete darkness. A large iris aperture admits more light and because this is an absolute effect the smaller Megachiroptera have disproportionately large eyes for their

Flying fox *Rousettus aegypticus* giving birth.

size. Like owls, but unlike cats and other occasionally nocturnal animals, the iris closes to a circular hole in bright light. The optical system has a very short focal length, producing a small and therefore bright image. The retina consists only of rods, giving sensitive but color-blind vision, and is folded by conical elevations of the choroid layer behind it, presumably so that more light-sensitive cells can be accommodated on the area available. There are over 420 million rods per square inch (672,000 mm^2) but on average there is only one optic nerve fibre for every $300-400$ rod cells, thus allowing for great stimulation at low light intensities.

Only one kind of Megachiropteran is known to be able to fly safely in complete darkness. This is the genus *Rousettus* which has normal Megachiropteran eyes on which it relies whenever the light is adequate. When vision fails these bats are able to use acoustic guidance by making short, high-pitched sounds and detecting echoes from nearby objects. The sounds are made by clicking the

tongue, each time producing a short pulse at about $12-15$ KHz (1 KHz=one thousand cycles per second). These sounds are high-pitched but are clearly audible to most people and have a wavelength of about one inch ($2·2-2·75$ cm). Because the acuity of any echolocation system is limited by the transmitted wavelength, these bats possess only a low resolution system. But then their fruit food is large and can usually be found by vision and smell. The main advantage of echolocation is that *Rousettus* is able to penetrate into deep caves to roost in pro-tective darkness whereas most other Mega-chiroptera must roost in the open. A few other cave-living forms are known and some produce sounds in flight, so further investiga-tion may show that *Rousettus* is not unique among Megachiroptera in using echo-location.

Flight guidance in the Microchiroptera is quite different. The size of the eyes is vari-able, but while none is blind (as is often supposed), none appears to have night vision comparable with that of the Megachiroptera. Nearly a quarter of the species, from all major families, have been investigated and all are found to emit a constant train of sound pulses during flight or even when active on the ground. These pulses differ from those of *Rousettus* in being produced vocally from the modified voice-box and in being almost entirely ultrasonic—that is, too high in pitch to be audible to man although their intensities may be very high. The actual sound frequencies range from about 15 KHz (just audible) to 150 KHz, having wave-lengths of $\frac{5}{6}$ to $\frac{1}{12}$ in ($2·2-0·22$ cm), although these extremes are rare and $20-100$ KHz is more usual. The sound pulses also vary in duration from about $\frac{1}{4}$ millisecond to as much as 60 millisecond.

These characteristics are potentially capable of great sensitivity and resolution which are clearly realized in practice. Insecti-vorous species have been shown to be capable of detecting and avoiding wires only 4 thousandths of an inch thick (0·1 mm) even in the presence of considerable back-ground noise. Moreover they detect, locate and intercept their insect prey in mid-air by this acoustic method, a task that is ap-parently too difficult for even the best night vision. Many nocturnal insects, however, are able to counteract this danger. Lacewings and several groups of moths have been shown to have 'ears' in various parts of their bodies which detect the ultra-sonic cries of bats and enable them to take evasive action. One group of moths even 'answers back' with its own train of ultrasonic pulses if a bat gets too close. This appears to deter the bat by advertising the moth's distastefulness much as warning colouration is shown by some daytime animals.

It is not yet clear to what extent the

non-insectivorous bats use their echolocation system in finding food. In all but the fish-catching bats the ultrasounds have a much lower intensity and may therefore be used only for obstacle avoidance, fruit and flowers being found by smell and vertebrate prey by sight and by passive listening as in owls. Fish location is even more puzzling since echolocation through the water surface is scarcely feasible, yet intense sounds are not required merely to maintain a constant low altitude over the surface. It seems probable that shoals of fish are located acoustically if they break the surface or jump and that individuals are seized by touch as the bats' feet trail through the water.

It is quite clear that echolocation works in different ways in different bats, for considerable variations are seen and some species change their behaviour under different circumstances. The emitted signals follow a number of frequency patterns: the shorter pulses are almost entirely of changing frequency, sweeping downwards by as much as a factor of three; some longer pulses merely sweep more slowly but more commonly a period of constant frequency is added to the sweep. Radar theory shows that short sweeps are ideal for measuring distance accurately whereas long constant notes can measure speed of movement instead. There is now good evidence that bats exploit these properties to the full.

Other features of echolocation behaviour also vary. The advanced species all tend to produce a pure note whereas primitive ones emit a complex series of harmonics. The primitive Emballonuroidea and the advanced Vespertilionoidea, with very few exceptions, open their mouths and 'shout' their pulses whereas the Rhinolophoidea and, with few exceptions, the Phyllostomatoidea all 'hum' through their noses. In all the latter bats the nostrils are surrounded by a very variable structure of naked skin known as the nose-leaf. This appears to influence the directional pattern of sound emission, but it has nothing to do with reception of echoes, which is done by the ears.

The hearing of Microchiropteran bats is naturally highly specialized. The auditory centres of the brain are relatively enormous to interpret the echoes that are essential to survival. The cochlea and middle-ear structures are highly modified in order to extend their sensitivity to high frequencies and the external ears are well developed as directional sound collectors although their appearance varies considerably. They may be enormous and joined together over the forehead or separate at the sides of the head, simple in form or folded into complex shapes. There is often a separate lobe or earlet, the tragus, in front of the ear itself. In most bats the ears are relatively immobile on the head and in some long-eared bats even a slight distortion of the ears causes considerable disorientation in flight. Yet the Rhinolophidae and the Hipposideridae 'wiggle' their ears vigorously, synchronizing the movements to the production of pulses, and are disorientated if these movements are prevented. In many Phyllostomatidae the ears are also mobile, but this appears not to be connected with echolocation.

In conclusion it may be said that almost every aspect of bat biology is unique and fascinating. But much knowledge of their physiology and habits is very recent and many problems remain. Even the number of species still undiscovered is likely to be high and the group as a whole deserves much further study. ORDER: Chiroptera, CLASS: Mammalia. J.D.P

Flying fox *Hypsignathus monstrosus* suckling its baby.

BATS AS DEVILS. In only a few places, such as China, have bats been considered as good omens. They are usually considered to be evil, their leathery wings being attributed to devils and witches, while angels are given feathery birds' wings. The Tomb bats must represent the peak of the link between bats and the dead and the painting of one, *Taphozous perforatus,* has been found in an Egyptian tomb dated 2,000 BC. To the bats, tombs are presumably another form of cave in which to roost but even in this century they have been linked to a strange legend. In 1922 the tomb of Tutankhamen was found in the Valley of Kings. Shortly afterwards, Lord Carnarvon and other members of the excavating team died and it was said that this was because they had committed sacrilege. A more rational suggestion put forward is that they caught histoplasmosis, a fungus disease, carried by bats and known to be fatal to man.

BEACONFISH *Hemigrammus ocellifer,* a small fish from the Amazon Basin and Guyana· with the alternative and equally appropriate name of Head-and-tail-light fish. It grows to $1\frac{3}{4}$ in (4·5 cm) and is one of the commonest aquarium fishes imported into Europe and the United States. The common name refers to the shining green-gold patch on the shoulder and a second patch at the base of the tail. The species is easy to breed (see under characins) and the sexes can be more easily distinguished than in many other members of the family Characidae. The male is the slimmer of the two and its swimbladder is quite clearly visible when the fish is viewed against a light; in the female the swimbladder is masked. FAMILY: Characidae, ORDER: Cypriniformes, CLASS: Pisces.

BEADLE G. W., American geneticist. In 1940, working with the chemist E. Tatum (a fellow Nobel Laureate), he abandoned the classical Fruit fly for experimentation and turned to the Red bread mould *Neurospora crassa.* They exposed mould colonies to X-rays, inducing mutations, and found that certain mutants were unable to synthesize certain enzymes, thus establishing the principle: one gene, one enzyme. Further studies confirmed and extended the connexion between the genes and metabolic processes. Subsequently, as an administrator, Beadle has contributed significantly to the development of the Biology Department of the California Institute of Technology.

BEADLET ANEMONE *Actinia equina,* one of a genus of Sea anemones. The species are all very similar and *Actinia equina* is widely distributed around the British Isles, Europe and down the west coast of Africa to just north of the Equator. It is one of the most familiar animals of the rocky shore, generally seen when the tide is out as a contracted, red-brown mass of stiff jelly about $1\frac{1}{4}$ in (3 cm) high. This anemone is found at all levels on the shore, often in situations where it is exposed to the air for long periods when the tide is out. It is able to withstand a considerable degree of desiccation, unusual for a marine animal which lacks any particular adaptations. Its habitat is very varied and it can tolerate estuarine conditions where the salinity may be lowered. The Beadlet anemone, when expanded, is a relatively short anemone with a smooth, soft body. The numerous tentacles are arranged in five circles and on the column below the tentacles is a ring of 24 clear blue spots. These are characteristic and enable one to make a correct identification on the shore. The colour of the whole animal varies from crimson through brown to green, and there are very pale specimens which may be yellow. One variety, known as the 'strawberry' variety, is crimson with green spots. The species is viviparous, rarely reproducing asexually. Sperm are released into the sea, which enter another anemone · and fertilize the ova. FAMILY: Actiniidae, ORDER: Actiniaria, CLASS: Anthozoa, PHYLUM: Cnidaria. S.E.H.

BEAKED SALMON *Gonorhynchus gonorhynchus,* a marine fish related to the milkfish but with certain anatomical peculiarities that place it in a separate family of its own. It is in no way related to the salmons. It is a slender fish with the mouth set below the pointed snout with a conspicuous barbel in front and the body covered with rough-edged scales which reach onto the head. It reaches 2 ft (60 cm) in length and is found in sandy areas from shallow water down to 500 ft (150 m) off the coasts of South Africa, Australia, New Zealand and Japan. In New Zealand, where it is fished for and considered a delicacy, the Beaked salmon is said to burrow swiftly into the sand with its snout. In South Africa, where it is sometimes brought in by trawlers, it is considered inedible. FAMILY: Gonorhynchidae, ORDER: Gonorhynchiformes, CLASS: Pisces.

BEAKED WHALES, Toothed whales that, with the Bottlenosed whales, make up the family Ziphiidae. Some of the family are reasonably well known but a number are described only from a few or even single skulls. In general they are born toothless but the males later develop a pair of teeth in the lower jaw, the females remaining essentially

toothless. Rows of small vestigial teeth are, however, often found in both upper and lower jaws.

There are two species of Bottlenosed whales, a well known northern form *Hyperoodon rostratus* and the little known southern *H. planifrons*. The northern Bottlenosed whale is of truly whale proportions, males reaching 30 ft (10 m) and females 24 ft (8 m). The body is dark grey to black dorsally and light grey ventrally. The dorsal fin, as with all known members of the family, is well behind the middle of the body, virtually at the junction with the tail. The head has a prominent beak and above it a very rounded dome which contains an oil reservoir, big enough for the animal to be hunted in the late 19th century for the spermaceti in it.

It is a fairly common species moving in small schools of 4–12 animals and feeding mainly on cuttlefish. It is occasionally stranded on British coasts, probably as it moves between northern waters, where it spends the summer, and the warmer water where it winters.

Similar in external appearance to the Bottlenosed whales are the two species of the

genus *Berardius*, *B. bairdi* and *B. arnuxi*, the former from the northern Pacific and the latter from the southern hemisphere. They are so little known that they have no popular name. The northern animal grows to a size of over 40 ft (13 m) whilst the southern is some 10 ft (3 m) smaller. Cuvier's beaked whale *Ziphius cavirostris* is rather better known. The head has a much less pronounced dome. The colour varies markedly and the description of 'purplish-black above, brown on the sides, and white below, except for the tail, where it was brown,' of a New Zealand specimen might not fit one in British waters. One described there had a cream white head, lower jaw and belly, with a dark back. Cuvier's beaked whale grows to about 23 ft (7.5 m). In spite of being fairly common throughout the world very little is known of its activities. The genus *Mesoplodon* is one of which nine species are described but only one, Sowerby's whale *M. bidens*, is at all well-known. It is found in the North Atlantic and is occasionally stranded on British coasts. It grows to a length of 15–16 ft (5 m) and has a slender, tapering head. Probably some of the species are of relatively local distribution which may account in part for the lack of knowledge.

Finally among the Beaked whales is a species, *Tasmacetus shepherdi,* of which one specimen was stranded in New Zealand in 1937 and is known only from this specimen and a lower jaw of unknown history. Although fitting in with the general pattern its teeth are more developed: 52 in the lower jaw and 38 in the upper but with the usual large pair at the tip of the lower jaw. Nothing more is known of it. See Toothed whales. FAMILY: Ziphiidae, ORDER: Cetacea, CLASS: Mammalia. K.M.B.

The Beadlet anemone *Actinia equina* with newly-budded off baby anemones.

BEAKED WHALE MYSTERIES. None of the Beaked whales is well known and some are known from a few specimens only. *Mesoplodon europaeus,* for example, is known from three specimens, one found floating in the English Channel, two cast up on the coast of New Jersey, USA. *M. stejnegeri* is known from two specimens from the Pacific coast of North America. *M. bowdoini* is known from two skeletons found on the coasts of New Zealand. *M. densirostris* is known from seven specimens taken in the Pacific, Indian and Atlantic Oceans, from places as far apart as Lord Howe Island, between Australia and New Zealand, and the coast of New Jersey. It is highly likely that others have been stranded or washed ashore on lonely parts of the coast and have not been recorded. The probability is that none of these species is really rare. So we have to ask why they are so seldom seen. One suggestion offered is that they are nocturnal. Another, that their normal haunts are in mid-ocean, away from shipping routes. A third, that they are seen but not recognized because they expose so little of themselves at the surface. There are parallels in the stories of the False killer whale (see Killer whale) and the Slender blackfish (see Pilot whales), species relatively unknown which suddenly are met in schools of many individuals. The same could conceivably happen with any one of the species of Beaked whales: that suddenly a whole school may be encountered somewhere in the world.

BEAR BAITING, a bloody spectacle in which a bear, chained to a post in the centre of an arena, or bear garden, was harassed by specially trained dogs encouraged to bite and torment it. In Britain, the popularity of this entertainment lasted for several hundreds of years until it was banned, for reasons of excessive cruelty, by an act of parliament in 1835.

BEARS, the world's largest terrestrial carnivores, so alike in appearance that they hardly can be confused with any other mammal. Characterized by their heavy build, thick limbs, diminutive tail and small ears, the members of the Ursidae comprise seven genera and nine species. Bears have a wide distribution which covers the northern hemisphere and overlaps in a few places in the southern hemisphere. Fossil remains exist in Africa and until quite recently a species lived in the Atlas mountains of Morocco. The different genera are mainly distinguished by small details of their skeletons. The fur is coarse and thick, and, with the exception of the Polar bear, dark in colour. The tuberculous molars indicate an omnivorous diet while the plantigrade walk (the whole sole of the foot resting on the ground with each step) is an ancestral trait which has been retained, giving the bear a slow and ponderous gait but when pursuing or pursued it will gallop. Some species climb well.

The eyes and ears are small and of all the senses smell is the sharpest and vision the least acute. Usually peaceful and timid creatures, bears may become formidable when wounded or suddenly disturbed, using their claws and teeth in conjunction with their great strength. Solitary and nocturnal, bears wander over their territory, the cubs remaining with the mother until half-grown. Species living in colder areas may become lethargic during the winter, but true hibernation does not take place, only a winter dormancy, as physiological body functions remain the same.

North American Black bear.

The cubs are very small at birth, weighing approximately 1/350th of the adult weight. Gestation varies between six to nine months long and delayed implantation occurs in most species, so the fragile young are born during 'hibernation', emerging from the den two or three months later. Sexual maturity is reached at two years for the females and up to six years for the males. The total life span can attain 40 years under ideal captive conditions, but in the more arduous wild environment, it is less than half of that.

The European Brown bear *Ursus arctos,* the most widespread species, has a typically short neck and large dog-like head. The grizzly, an American subspecies, is the largest terrestrial member of the Carnivora, some individuals reaching 113 in (280 cm) in length and weighing over 1,700 lb (780 kg) but 80 in (200 cm) and 550 lb (250 kg) are more usual measurements. Coat colouration varies from cream to blue-black. Distributed across Alaska and Canada down to the western portion of North America, it is also found in the mountains of Europe and Asia Minor, across to the Himalayas. Once known as *Ursus horribilis,* the grizzly has the reputation of being particularly ferocious. Because bears have few vocalizations and no facial expressions, they do not give a warning sound or posture such as those which we have come to recognize in dogs, for instance. For this reason, they have been labelled 'unpredictable brutes'. The strength of the Brown bear is proverbial, sometimes killing an adult cow with a swipe of the forepaw and dragging the carcass back to the den. In certain areas fish are scooped out of the stream and form a large part of the diet. Fruit and grass are eaten in the spring as a laxative when the bears become active again after 'hibernating'.

The North American Black bear *Euarctos americanus* was until recently classified as *Ursus.* It is, however, smaller than the Brown bear, rarely measuring more than 70 in (180 cm) in length or weighing over 330 lb (150 kg). Different colourations exist: black, cinnamon and even white. The muzzle is often brown. The paws, which are less massive make this species particularly agile and full-grown adults can still climb trees. Breeding takes place in June or July but the fertilized egg does not become implanted in the uterine wall until November. One to four cubs are then born in January or February and remain with the mother until the following autumn.

The Spectacled bear *Tremarctos ornatus* is the only South American species, living both in low forests and up to 1,000 ft (300m) in the Andean mountains. Although once widely distributed from Peru across to Venezuela and Ecuador, this relatively small bear is now considered rare. Measuring 60–70 in (150–180 cm), adults weigh up to 300 lb (140 kg) but the shaggy coat contributes to the bulky appearance. Some individuals have uneven white streaks circling the eyes and extending to the muzzle, down the throat to the chest, while others are completely dark brown-black. Unlike northern species, the Spectacled bear, in the wild at least, has a remarkably uniform diet of grass, fruit or nutritious roots, depending on the locality. While foraging, it is said to climb trees, knocking down fruit and branches alike or tearing the soft bark with its claws. One cub is born after a gestation of eight to nine months.

This map emphasizes how the bulk of bears are north of the equator.

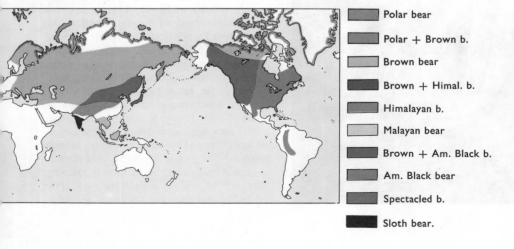

Polar bear
Polar + Brown b.
Brown bear
Brown + Himal. b.
Himalayan b.
Malayan bear
Brown + Am. Black b.
Am. Black bear
Spectacled b.
Sloth bear.

Polar bear twins. In the wild Polar bear cubs are born in winter in the mother's hide-out in the snow.

A Brown bear of the northern hemisphere.

The Polar bear *Thalarctos maritimus* is the only completely carnivorous bear. Its year-round cream colour is perfect camouflage, blending with the background of ice floes in the Arctic. Among other characteristics, this large bear has a more slender and longer neck than the Brown or Black bears. The soles of the feet are thickly haired, providing both insulation and a secure grip on the ice. Furthermore, the forepaws are partially webbed and the neck and shoulder muscles greatly developed, making the Polar bear a tireless swimmer. Attaining occasionally 9 ft (200–280 cm) in length, the weight oscillates between 800 and 1,550 lb (400–700 kg) depending on the season. Nomadic in the extreme, Polar bears are sometimes discovered resting on ice floes 200 miles (320 km) at sea. Should these precarious havens melt, the bears are reported to be swimming 'in the middle of nowhere' but are actually heading for the nearest shore. In rough water, they swim with eyes and nose submerged but the 'dog-paddle', with head above water, is more commonly used. A bear at sea is as defenceless as a seal on land and, while it rarely ventures more than a mile or two inland when using overland short-cuts, it prefers a strictly coastal existence.

Seals are the main prey. The bear waits for the seal to surface at its breathing hole in the ice then grabs it and hauls it out. 30 lb (13 kg) of seal blubber (rather than the flesh) can be eaten at one sitting. Mating occurs in mid-April or May and while tracking the solitary females over great distances, the males become extremely irascible both towards other males and humans. In winter, the females excavate a shallow den under the snow and there the cubs are born in January. Blind and helpless, the young are the size of a Guinea pig at birth. The mother does not leave this makeshift shelter, living off her fat reserves, until the cubs can follow her about. When they emerge during the early summer months, the young Polar bears are weaned on

berries and Arctic hares, waiting until the following winter to be initiated to the seal hunting technique. Because the cubs stay so long with the female, breeding takes place only every other year, which accounts for the low population numbers. Eskimos hunt these bears but do not eat the liver which contains poisonously large amounts of vitamin A, as in the shark. Now the Polar bear is tracked down by unsportsmanlike hunters in amphibious planes and shot while swimming. Its only natural enemies are the Killer whale and perhaps the walrus.

The Himalayan bear *Selenarctos thibetanus* occurs in the elevated forests of Baluchistan, Afghanistan, westward to the Himalayas and northwards into China and Siberia. Its coat is black (or brown during the summer moult) and the white chevron fur pattern stands out clearly on the chest. The tufted ears are relatively larger and the muzzle shorter than in the European Brown bear *Ursus arctos* but they share common behavioural traits. 'Moon' bears or 'Blue' bears, as they are also called, descend to the valleys to spend the winter and do not 'hibernate', becoming intermittently dormant only during the height of a monsoon or a blizzard. Surprisingly enough, this heavy animal is an agile climber, building rough nests in low trees to sunbathe or nap. A den is preferred though when rearing cubs. Family parties have been observed foraging together

in fruit trees and it seems probable that the juveniles remain with the parents for at least a year, sometimes even after the next litter is born.

The Indian and Ceylonese Sloth bear *Melursus ursinus* is quite different from other Asiatic bears. The muzzle is elongated into a snout which shows great lateral mobility. Smaller and even shaggier than the Himalayan Black bear, it has a mantle of long, coarse fur on its shoulders, giving it a humped appearance. There is also a wide, often semi-circular shaped yellowish expanse of fur on the chest but the overall colouration varies from reddish-brown to black. It weighs 200–240 lb (90–110 kg) and measures 56–70 in (140–180 cm) in length. Solitary and nocturnal, it spends most of the day sleeping in jungle caves. The outstanding behavioural trait of this bear is its method of feeding. Along with a long snout and extremely mobile lips, it has a gap in its front teeth, due to the absence of a pair of incisors in both upper and lower jaws. An observer in the field reports that after tearing a termite nest apart with its claws, this 'vacuum-cleaner' bear places its muzzle near the hole and sucks in the grubs with such force that the noise can be located 200 yd (180 m) away. Another dental characteristic is the small molars, indicating a diet of fruit and insects. After a seven month gestation, two or three cubs are born in the spring. Strangely enough they are carried on

A Grizzly bear watches a puma feeding. Although they are basically vegetarian, grizzlies will readily eat flesh, either freshly killed or as carrion.

Polar bears following each other ashore after a swim off the coast of northern Canada.

the mother's back during her nightly rounds and when climbing up a tree. Later, even when several months old the young, if suddenly alarmed, scramble over each other to reach this safe vantage point, now with room only for one.

The Sun bear *Helarctus malayanus* of Malaya looks like a diminutive, short-haired version of the South American Spectacled bear but the chest and eye patches when present are usually of a tan colour. This is the smallest member of the bear family, measuring 44–56 in (110–140 cm) and weighing 50–140 lb (22–65 kg) at the most. It occurs in the forests of Burma down the Malaya Peninsula to Sumatra and Borneo. The large feet with crescent-shaped claws and naked soles are arboreal adaptations as this bear spends most of the day sleeping or sunbathing in crudely made nests above the ground, similar to those fashioned by the Himalayan bear. On the ground, it has a rolling, shuffling gait reminiscent of the Lesser panda *Ailurus* which also walks with forepaws turned inwards. The claws are used, when feeding, to scatter fruit or tear open bee hives and termite hills. Afterwards, the bear licks up the insects among the debris with its long prehensile tongue. Small rodents, birds and eggs also complement the diet of this omnivore. Sun bears make amusing pets when young but their intelligence turns to cunning with age and they become dangerously irascible if confined. One or two cubs are born in September after an undetermined gestation period and follow the parents until fully grown. FAMILY: Ursidae, ORDER: Carnivora, CLASS: Mammalia.　　　　　N.D.

BEARS, an old legend was that bear cubs were born in a shapeless mass and were licked into shape by their mother. Thus, Alexander Pope writes:

> 'So watchful Bruin forms, with plastic care,
> Each growing lump, and brings it to a bear.'

From this comes the modern phrase of 'to lick into shape' meaning to train or to put in order. As with many old ideas about animal behaviour there is a grain of truth because bears, like many other mammals, are born blind and naked and the mother has to lick the enveloping birth membranes from them.

BEAVERS, largest rodents in the northern hemisphere, sometimes exceeding 88 lb (40 kg). The heavy body is covered with a thick fur making a waterproof coat, which the fair sex usually only knows by its undercoat when the tanner has removed the kemp, the long guard hairs which protect the undercoat from wear and water. The hind paws are large and webbed to the tips of the five toes. The second toe has a double nail, similar to a bird's beak, which acts as a fine comb. The hindquarters are very powerful in contrast to the small forelimbs, which barely touch the ground when it is moving along. All orifices can be closed when the beaver is under water including the cloaca, which is closed over the ano-urino-genital organs. The tail is an indispensable counterpoise on land and a horizontal rudder when the animal is in the water, with a heavy burden in its arms. The lips close behind the incisors, protecting the mucous membranes from water and from splinters of wood while the animal is working under water. The front paws, which are veritable hands, nimble and skilful, carry, push, pull, steer, scratch and groom. The beaver's respiratory system enables it to remain under water for up to 15 minutes.

Finally, its brain is smooth, so the beaver is known as lissencephalic, but includes a cortex which compensates in thickness (from this aspect it is classified at the top of all rodents) for what it lacks in surface folds. That is, although the surface of the brain is smooth the beaver does not lack intelligence and is placed above all other rodents.

Before man became a dangerous rival, beavers lived all over the northern hemisphere, each kind in its respective continent. Scientists make a distinction between two kinds, the European *Castor fiber* and the American *C. canadensis,* but it takes an expert eye to tell them apart. Moreover, both types can be crossed and produce fertile hybrids, which, unfortunately, has happened all over Finland. The two types are known as 'geographical' types, in order to emphasize that the infinitesimal differences to be found are due to their (relatively recent) spatial separation. Since then they have become more rare, because of hunting and trapping, they have disappeared from many regions, although the total area of distribution has changed very little. Fortunately, energetic steps taken for their preservation and re-colonization during the last few decades have given them back to the U.S.A., Norway, Sweden and the U.S.S.R. There are still a few hundreds (or thousands) in France, Eastern Germany and Poland. They have just been reintroduced into Switzerland with some chances of success.

They have been known to live for 30 years and more in zoos. Although a beaver can breed from the age of two years, it is not at that time fully grown. A beaver and its mate seem to remain together for a long time, if not for their entire life. Both defend their common territory from outsiders of their own kind. The mating season is in February, when the winter ice is melting; the beavers pair under water, *more humano,* or even at the edge of

the water. About 100 days later young are born, fluffy and resourceful, eyes already open. A litter averages three young. The mother keeps them in the burrow for two or three weeks, together with last year's young, while the father and the two-year olds leave the burrow, the father to stay nearby, the others to start on the great adventure. It is not true that the parents turn out the young that

European beaver in Scandinavia, one of its few remaining strongholds in Europe outside the Soviet Union.

have reached sexual maturity. The father returns to the conjugal home when the youngest begin to move around outside. The young are suckled during this period of confinement only, but the mother brings them tender young leaves a few days after birth. If by chance the young escape from the burrow through gaps in the walls, or even through the diving hole, the mother brings them back at once, walking semi-erect and carrying them between her chin and her arms. The young remain under their parents' tutelage, disturbing them more by their restlessness than helping by their presence. They chatter a lot,

particularly inside the burrow; their cries are at first rather like those of puppies, then like human infants. As they grow up they become less and less talkative. Communication is chiefly by smell or gestures, aimed at the identification of individuals, the establishment and preservation of a hierarchy (where the female takes the prior position), warning of danger (by a stroke of the tail reverberating on the surface of the water) and generally speaking conveying the mood than actual information with the object of constructive action. The secretion of the 'castoreum' glands placed on the bank of the river at well-chosen spots, marks out the individual territory and is effective in discouraging outsiders.

The beaver is superior to all other mammals in the efficiency and technical skill used in organizing its domain. It prefers to settle on shallow lowland streams, where there is plenty of vegetation, and by means of dams converts them into a series of water-levels, the value of which is obvious; they provide protection from enemies coming from the river banks and an easy and rapid means of getting around. Furthermore, by keeping the water at a constant level, they camouflage the underwater entrance to their burrow and ensure access to their winter stores, even if the surface of the water is frozen. Although, during the summer months, the beavers live on all kinds of plant life, during the hard weather they have to live on the bark of the willows and poplars which they have collected in front of the entrance. The food eaten during the night passes through a first digestive process (particularly due to the bacteria of the caecum); collected the next day in the cloaca it is only assimilated when it passes into the digestive tube for the second time (caecotrophy).

The beaver's shelter may be merely a cavity dug in the steep bank of the river

Schematic view of a beaver dam and lodge. The technical skill in such construction work is, among mammals, only rivalled by that of man.

starting from a sloping gallery which begins just below the surface of the water. If the banks are too low, the beavers build a lodge, a wooden dome consolidated with mud and having a diameter of up to 18–20 ft (6–7 m). The largest lodges may have several rooms, each having an independent gallery. Inside, the nest may be seen, provided with a bedding of dry shredded wood. Each family has several homes, inhabited successively apparently according to whim.

The most surprising piece of work is the dam, which may reach enormous widths, up

Canadian beaver in its pond.

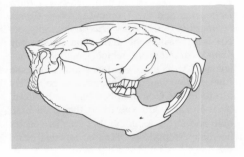

Skull of beaver showing powerful incisors.

Typical beaver pond and main dam, constructed of branches and logs plastered with mud.

to more than 1,000 yd (1,000 m). In spite of their size they are never the work of enormous colonies, at most two or three families living amicably together, since they are of the same blood. A family rarely exceeds ten members.

The communications network is almost entirely aquatic, except for a few short straight paths towards the felled trees. If it is necessary to go farther the beavers can dig long canals, where they feel safer than on shore.

The work is done in accordance with innate behaviour patterns which can easily be observed in young animals that have been kept away from their kind since birth. Nevertheless, in addition to instinctive 'knowledge' the beaver must be credited with powers of intelligence which enable it to solve the most difficult problems with which the researchers confront it ('detour' experiments) and which nature also sometimes has up its sleeve. FAMILY: Castoridae, ORDER: Rodentia, CLASS: Mammalia.   P.B.R.

BEAVER SCENT, or castoreum, is a syrupy substance secreted from glands at the base of the tail and used by beavers to mark their territory. From the time of the Ancient Greeks it has been collected for use as a medicine in the treatment of a wide variety of disorders including hysteria and palpitations of the heart. Modern chemical analysis has shown that it contains salicylic acid, the principal ingredient of aspirin. Although

castoreum is secreted by both male and female beavers, the ancients believed that it was secreted in the testes. Physiologus, author of one of the earliest bestiaries, describes how a beaver will, when he is chased, bite off his testicles and throw them to his hunters. If he is chased a second time he lifts his tail to show that he is not worth pursuing.

BED-BUGS, cosmopolitan blood-sucking insects associated with man and many animals, including birds and bats. They are true bugs, that is, they are members of the order Hemiptera. The Common bed-bug *Cimex lectularius* and the Tropical bed-bug *Cimex rotundatus* (=*C. hemipterus*) commonly occur as parasites of man. The pigeon-bug *Cimex columbarius,* which lives closely associated with pigeons, doves and Domestic fowl, is now usually considered to be merely a race of the Common bed-bug, and indeed, the two races are known to thrive on both man and birds. A similar, but smaller species normally found in House martins' and swallows' nests will also bite man.

The adult bed-bug is flat and roughly oval in shape, being about $\frac{1}{5}$ in (5 mm) long and $\frac{1}{8}$ in (3 mm) broad. The body is covered with fine short hairs and is usually mahogany brown, but it may appear more reddish if it has recently fed or purple if an older meal is still present in its gut. Immature bed-bugs (usually called nymphs) are paler in colour than adults. When in need of a meal bed-bugs are paper-thin but appear much fatter, even almost globular after a large meal. They have lost the ability to fly and all that remains of the once functional wings are a pair of short flaps on the middle segment of the thorax.

The Common bed-bug is found throughout Europe, Russia, northern India, North Africa, North and South America and Australia. This species tends to be replaced in the tropics by the Tropical bed-bug which is much better adapted to high temperatures, but is otherwise very similar to the Common bed-bug. The fact that several species of bed-bugs feed on birds and bats, which habitually breed in caves or rock clefts, suggests that man and the Common bed-bug may have commenced their 'partnership' when man himself inhabited caves. But we shall probably never know for certain the original habitat of the bed-bug. As it has been carried by commerce all over the world wherever suitable conditions occur, its primary centre of distribution is also something of a mystery. Most authorities consider the Middle East as the most likely area of origin, especially on the eastern Mediterranean coasts. The insects were known to the Romans and Ancient Greeks who regarded them as having wide medicinal properties when taken in a draft of water or wine.

Bed-bugs were recorded from the area now known as Germany in the 11th century, but apparently did not invade Britain until the early 16th century and Sweden until the 1800's. The first records of bed-bugs from England were in ports, particularly London, and today they are still commonest in such coastal areas, probably due to repeated re-introductions from ships. The remainder of this account refers mainly to the Common bed-bug, although most of what is said is equally applicable to the tropical species.

After mating the female bed-bug lays up to 150–200 eggs at the rate of two or three per day. Each egg is creamy white, slightly curved

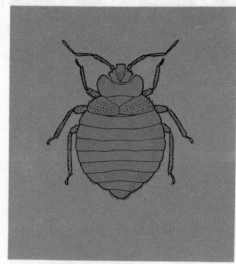

Adult male Bed bug.

and elongated in form, with a lid or operculum at one end, and is about $\frac{1}{25}$ in (1 mm) long. They are deposited in crevices and cracks, behind skirtingboards, wall paper and similar sites, each being firmly fixed in place with a glue-like secretion produced by the accessory glands of the female reproductive apparatus. The eggs require a temperature of at least 55°F (13°C) to hatch. At 82°F (28°C) they will hatch in five or six days. When fully developed the tiny nymph forces off the operculum and emerges as a miniature of the adult, about the size of a pin head. It moults its skin and forms a new, larger skin to accommodate each of five increases in size between egg and adult. Each nymphal stage needs at least one full blood meal before proceeding to the next growth stage, but additional blood meals may occasionally be taken.

The bed-bug sucks the blood of its human host using a rostrum or jointed beak beneath its head. When not in use the rostrum is carried pointing backwards under the head, but it is swung forwards and extended when the bug feeds. The rostrum is composed of two pairs of needle-like stylets which are supported by a jointed lower lip (the labium). The two pairs of stylets when pressed together

form two tubes, a larger one for sucking up blood and a smaller one through which saliva is pumped into the wound. A hungry bed-bug carefully selects a suitable area of the skin with delicate probing movements of the rostrum and then penetrates the skin using the serrated tips of the stylets, so that these come to rest in a blood capillary. Saliva is pumped through the insect's mouthparts into the capillary from the salivary glands in the thorax. A mixture of blood and saliva is then sucked up the food canal in the stylets and passed into the gut. The saliva prevents coagulation of the host's blood and hence clogging of the delicate stylet mechanism and the gut is avoided. The intense irritation which is well known to accompany bed-bug bites is apparently caused by the saliva, the wound made by the stylets being a very minor puncture. Some people seem to be very much more sensitive to bug bites than others and many tend to lose their sensitivity if bitten repeatedly. A feeding bed-bug may take up to 12 min (frequently less) to fully gorge itself, depending, apparently, on the size of the blood capillary penetrated by the tip of the stylets. After feeding the bug takes on an extremely bloated appearance, having imbibed up to six times its own weight of blood. Feeding normally occurs about once a week in summer, less frequently in cooler weather, and probably not at all in unheated premises in the winter in Britain.

Bed-bugs are chiefly nocturnal and are probably only seen in broad daylight if very hungry. They are said to be most lively just before dawn and it may be supposed that those seen walking in daylight are individuals that have failed to secure a suitable blood meal in the normal hours of activity. Bed-bugs may be said to be truly blood-thirsty animals as all the evidence indicates that they only feed on the blood of birds and mammals. Under laboratory conditions they can be induced to feed through a membrane simulating the host's skin. It is interesting to note that a bug steadfastly refuses to feed from otherwise suitable fluids unless skin or some other substitute membrane is present to be pierced initially.

Adult bed-bugs can live for four years with occasional feeds and can fast completely for one year. In general they survive longest if living under relatively cool conditions. Although primarily a parasite on man, bed-bugs may successfully feed on rabbits, mice, rats and birds if human blood is not readily available. They are, therefore, to be reckoned as highly successful parasites as they do not cause the host very great harm and can adapt to other hosts if necessary. Substantial populations of bugs thrive best in centrally-heated buildings such as large blocks of flats where winter temperatures, particularly in bedrooms, are never very low. In unheated premises established populations of bugs will always suffer a very great reduction in numbers in winter. Under these conditions they breed only in the summer and only the adults and older nymphs survive the winter. Thus very high densities of bed-bugs are unlikely to be found in ordinary dwelling houses without central heating in temperate climates, but unless a careful watch is kept for them they may infest centrally-heated flats in which standards of hygiene are low on a large scale.

Bed-bugs are attracted by the heat and smell of their hosts. Experimental evidence suggests, however, that they may only detect the warmth of their hosts when quite near, as a tube of warm water will be approached by a hungry insect only if it is at a distance of 3 in ($7\frac{1}{2}$ cm) or less. The hungry bug may investigate the nature of such a warm object by repeated probing with the rostrum before rejecting it and this suggests that an olfactory (smell) sense may be most active only at very close quarters. Bed-bugs also tend to aggregate in places previously occupied by members of their own species, since they also seem to react positively to secretions and excretions of other bed-bugs. Like many bugs, bed-bugs have a pungent odour which is produced by so-called 'stink glands' in the last segment of the thorax. To most people this smell is not too unpleasant and the 'buggy' smell of bed-bug infested houses is usually due to a variety of causes associated with a gross neglect of general and personal hygiene, and not to the bugs themselves.

The frequently heard story of bed-bugs reaching their sleeping victims by dropping onto them from the ceiling is apparently well substantiated, but it is not known how the bugs detect the host's presence. Deliberate attempts to prevent bugs reaching their hosts by standing the legs of the bed in containers of oil or water may fail not only because of this unpleasant behaviour pattern but because the bugs may be hidden in the frame of the bed or fabric of the mattress where they are exceedingly difficult to detect. Although the bed-bug cannot scale a perfectly smooth surface such as glass, polished wood or metal, it can utilize a film of grime or a corroded surface. Normally a sluggish insect, the bed-bug has been credited with incredible speeds but its fastest reliably recorded speed seems to be about 40 in (102 cm) per min which is less than $\frac{1}{25}$ mph (0·06 kph).

It is often assumed that bed-bugs are only associated with old and dilapidated property, especially in slums, but in fact, they occur from time to time in all types of buildings inhabited or used by man, and amongst all classes of population whatever precautions are taken. The insect's natural mobility is aided by transport of furniture and bedding, purchase of second-hand furniture, bug-infested vans, storage of furniture and the use of timber from old houses that have been

demolished. They may appear in what seem to be the most unlikely places. The author remembers the unexpected appearance of a hungry adult bed-bug on a laboratory bench in a new building in a university. This starving insect which received a large meal from a sympathetic student, was kept as a living curiosity for some time. The American parasitologist, Chandler, recorded that newcomers to the tropics often wonder why their heads itch, until they discover a thriving colony of bugs in the ventilator at the top of their sun helmets.

Nowadays, it is generally accepted that, surprisingly, bed-bugs are not responsible for large outbreaks of epidemic disease. But there is evidence that they may harbour pathogenic organisms of several types although they rarely transmit the diseases to their hosts. Nevertheless, they may occasionally transmit serious diseases such as kala azar, Chagas' disease, plague, tularemia and relapsing fever in the tropics and subtropics. Although the bed-bug is apparently not a regular transmitter of diseases to man, the irritation from bites is likely to cause sleepless nights and hence to contribute to ill-health of both children and adults. Whilst small numbers of bed-bugs may be encountered anywhere where human beings live, the presence of large breeding populations of bugs indicates a lack of general hygiene. Viewed from this standpoint, bed-bugs are clearly most undesirable inhabitants of our dwellings.

The strict habit of personal and property cleanliness is certainly the best safeguard against infestation. Minor infestations may be quite adequately treated by thorough cleaning of the area concerned. Woodwork, and where possible furniture and walls, should be well washed with soap and water containing a

disinfectant. Upholstered furniture may have to be removed for disinfestation by fumigation, although the application of one of the many proprietary forms of aerosol-type insecticides is usually very effective. Pyrethrin-based insecticides are safest indoors, especially where food is handled. If a large scale bed-bug infestation is discovered it would normally be advisable to contact the local Medical Officer of Health. Properly qualified and equipped personnel are available to deal effectively with such situations by offering advice and practical assistance. ORDER: Hemiptera, CLASS: Insecta, PHYLUM: Arthropoda.   M.J.P.

A honeybee shown while collecting pollen from apple blossom.

BEE, flying insect of the order Hymenoptera. Bees differ from other members of this order in their habit of providing nectar and pollen for their young. In connection with this their bodies are covered with branched plumose hairs in which they trap pollen from flowers. Pollen collected in this way is later combed into specialized pollen carrying apparatus which often occurs on the hind legs, but also on other parts of the body (e.g. the megachiles or Leaf-cutting bees have a dense brush of hairs on the underside of the abdomen). The mouthparts of bees are interlocked and extended to form a tube for collecting nectar. The length of the tongue varies greatly from one species to another and helps to determine which flowers can be visited. Nectar is carried back to the nest in a special enlarged part of the foregut known as the honeystomach or crop.

Some bees, such as the well-known *bumblebees and *honeybees, are social and live together in colonies which consist of the mother and her adult and immature offspring. But the majority of the 19,000 or so species of bees are solitary in habit: the adult life of parent and offspring do not overlap, there is no co-operation between them and there is no worker caste. Some bee species (especially those belonging to the Halictidae) exhibit various stages in the beginnings of social life and, as it is difficult to classify them into either category, they are sometimes referred to as semi-social bees.

In general, solitary bees occur throughout the world, including the Arctic Circle, wherever there are suitable flowering plants and nesting sites, but they are most abundant in warm, arid semi-desert regions.

There is a great diversity in the nest sites of different species. Most solitary bees nest in the ground, but some, depending on the species, may choose soil that is clay · or sandy, loose or compact, open ground or protected and covered to varying degrees with vegetation. However, only well drained soil is suitable and the length of the main tunnel the bees excavate is determined to some extent by the moisture level in the soil. The length of the main shaft and the form of the tunnelling also differ according to the species. The cells in which the young are reared may occur in a linear series in the main shaft itself, or may be constructed at the end of short tunnels off the main shaft. The cells are lined with a thin layer of waterproof material. The surface-entrances to the tunnels are sometimes made conspicuous by hillocks or tumuli of the excavated soil.

Some solitary bees which nest above ground use the stems of plants such as bramble or raspberry, while others burrow into dead twigs and branches and excavate the soft pith or heartwood. For making and lining the cells mud or sections cut from leaves and flower petals are used.

It is essential the nest should be near suitable plants which provide the nectar and pollen fed to the larvae. Solitary bees practice mass provisioning. Each cell is provided with a lump of pollen, usually moistened with nectar, which takes several trips to collect. When the pollen lump is large enough the female lays an egg on it and seals the entrance to the cell. She then begins to work on provisioning another. Hence when the egg hatches the larva finds itself on a bed of pollen which has to provide for its entire development. The female that laid the egg has no contact with her growing young.

Development during the larval stage is very sensitive to change in humidity and if a pollen lump becomes too dry the larva feeding on it may die. This applies particularly to bees that nest underground where conditions are usually more constant than for bees nesting in plant material above the surface. Indeed it is possible to remove many megachiles from their cells and rear them on pollen lumps at room temperature and at a relative humidity greater than 50%.

After the larva has fed for a few weeks it is

Odours play a large part in the economy of a honeybee colony. This honeybee is shown while fanning its own scent onto the air with its wings.

fully grown and enters the prepupal or resting stage in which it is most resistant to variations in the temperature and other physical conditions of its environment. Many bees pass the winter, or other periods of unfavourable conditions, in the prepupal state. This usually lasts for nine or ten months, but in desert regions it may be several years before rainfall is sufficiently great to induce the bees to complete development. The return of favourable conditions is usually followed by a brief period of pupation and emergence. However, this is not invariably so and some species of *Andrena* are prepupae for a few weeks only before they pupate and they spend the winter in their cells as adults. Other bees (e.g. *Halictus*) may actually emerge from their cells in late summer and hibernate in the soil during the autumn and winter.

Males of solitary bees emerge in advance of females and, where the young develop in a linear series in tunnels or stems, the cells near the exit contain males. The early emergence of males is advantageous in enabling the females to become impregnated soon after they are active. Indeed males of some species patrol nesting sites for this purpose and mating sometimes takes place within the burrows. However, mating usually occurs near the

flowers from which the females are collecting pollen and the males restrict their activity or waiting to the plant species frequented by the females. Males of yet another species make patrolling flights along hedgerows and other vegetation not visited for food and presumably the two sexes meet along such flight paths. Copulation itself lasts only a few seconds.

Soon after copulation the females seek sites in which to begin their own nests. There is a tendency in many species of bees to return to the site from which they emerged. This gregarious habit may lead to large aggregations of bees in small areas (e.g. various species of *Andrena* and *Nomia*).

Some species of bees consistently collect food from one plant species only or from a group of related species. Such bees are said to be oligolectic. The time of emergence of the bee is usually synchronized to coincide with the flowering of its host plant and the bee's daily flight periods are often at the time that its host plant is presenting pollen for the day.

The social bees include the bumblebees (*Bombus*), the stingless bees (*Melipona* and *Trigona*) and the honeybees (*Apis*). Bumblebees occur in temperate climates and are relatively more abundant in the Arctic region

Above: A queen honeybee laying eggs attended by workers. Below: I. Buff-tailed bumblebee *Bombus terrestris*, female left, worker centre, male right; 2. Large red-tailed bumblebee *Bombus lapidarius*, female left, male right; 3. Hill cuckoo bee *Psithyrus rupestris*; 4. Carder bee *Bombus agrorum*, queen left, worker right; 5. Cuckoo bee *Coelioxys elongata*. All natural size.

than solitary bees, whereas the stingless bees are abundant in the tropics. Like the bumble-bees, the stingless bees have a horizontal comb, which contains separate cells for nectar and pollen storage and for the brood. There are three species of honeybee. The most widespread is *Apis mellifera*. Its ability to regulate the temperature and humidity of its nest, together with its ability to survive on stored food during unfavourable periods, has undoubtedly played a major part in its successful colonization of most of the world.

Each honeybee colony contains three castes: the mother or fertile female known as the 'queen', the infertile females known as 'workers' and the fertile males known as 'drones'. Usually there is only one queen to a colony but up to 60,000 workers. In natural conditions the nest of a honeybee colony consists of a series of vertical wax combs in a hollow tree or cave, or under an overhanging rock or some such shelter. On either side of each wax comb are series of hexagonal cells in which the young are reared and the honey and pollen are stored. Most of the tasks of the colony are done by workers. Those born in the spring and summer generally undertake a series of duties which are dependent to some extent on the development of certain glands in their bodies. Thus, at first they clean cells and remove debris, but after a few days special brood-food glands in their heads have developed sufficiently for them to feed a protein-rich secretion to the larvae. A few days later the wax glands, which are located on the underside of the abdomen, have developed sufficiently for them to secrete wax and build a comb. Other tasks done inside the nest include packing pollen loads into cells, receiving nectar from foragers, converting it into honey and guarding the entrance to the nests. The task done by a particular worker depends not only upon its physiological condition but also on the requirements of the colony at the time. Indeed a worker spends much of its time 'patrolling' the combs and so becomes aware of current needs. A worker first leaves its nest when only a few days old to make orientation flights during which it learns the location of its home in relation to that of surrounding landmarks and when it is about two to three weeks old it begins to forage. It continues to do so for the rest of its life, which may be only about four weeks in midsummer, but as long as six months for bees that emerged in late summer or autumn.

Like solitary bees and bumblebees, worker honeybees collect nectar and pollen, but they also, on occasion, collect propolis and water. Propolis is a sticky exudate of various buds and the bees use it to cement and block gaps in the covering to their nest and to reduce the size of the entrance. Water is used for cooling the nest as well as to dilute honey. To cool the nest the bees either spread it on the surface of

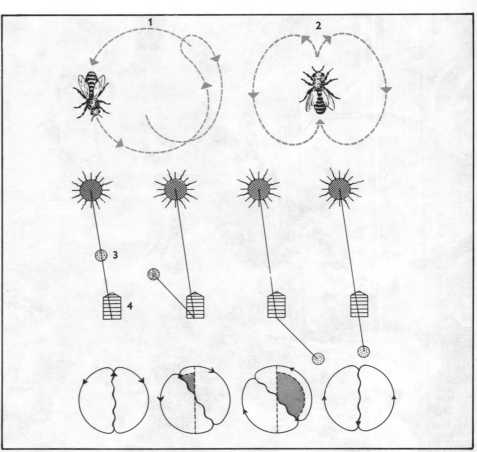

Language of bees: 1. round dance, for distances less than 50 m; 2. figure-of-eight dance, for distances over 100 m, the actual distance being indicated by the speed with which the abdomen is wagged, the greater the distance the more slowly it is wagged; 3. represents a source of nectar and 4. the hive, and in the bottom row is shown the pattern of the figure-of-eight dance according to the position of the source of nectar relative to the sun.

Honeybee drones contribute nothing to the colony except for mating with the queen (right).

the wax cells or manipulate it on their tongues to hasten its evaporation. They also aid cooling by fanning a current of air through the nest with their wings.

However, most foraging trips are for nectar or pollen or both. Although, unlike many solitary bees, honeybees do not restrict themselves to one or a few plant species, during any one foraging trip an individual bee tends to keep constant to one plant species only. Indeed they tend to become conditioned to make their flights at the time of day at which flowers of their particular species open or present pollen, at other times remaining inside their nest. Any fixation to a particular species is temporary only and should a species cease flowering, or for some other reason fail to yield nectar or pollen, the bees concerned will soon forsake it for another. Although some bees may find a particular source of forage for themselves, more often than not they are informed about it by others. The ability of bees to communicate a favourable source of forage is one of the most remarkable biological discoveries of this century. On its return home a successful forager performs a 'dance' on the surface of the comb, features of the dance indicating the direction of the food source in relation to the direction of the sun from the nest entrance and its distance from the nest. Bees that follow the dancing bee and receive the information are further helped to locate the food by the odour of the flowers that clings to the dancing bee's body.

The eagerness with which a dancing bee is followed, or with which the load of a successful forager is received, depends upon the extent of the colony's current need for the particular type of forage. Whereas nectar is welcome at any time, pollen demands are particularly high when brood rearing is extensive, and the amount collected is related to the size of the brood being reared.

In turn, egg-laying and brood-production are governed to a considerable extent by the amount of pollen a colony can collect. The queen is specialized for egg laying and, unlike the queen bumblebee, is incapable of doing the tasks of worker bees. Her egg production reaches its peak in late spring or early summer when she may lay about 1,500 eggs per day. To maintain such a rate of egg production, a large protein intake is necessary and the workers feed the queen entirely with glandular secretions to enable this to occur. The queen lays two types of egg, fertile eggs giving rise to workers or queens and unfertilized eggs giving rise to drones. The worker- and drone-producing eggs are laid one per cell, the drone-producing eggs in slightly larger cells than the worker-producing cells. The worker eggs hatch to larvae three days after they are laid, and after five days of feeding the larvae change into pupae and the top of the cells are covered with a cap of wax. The larvae are visited and fed a great many times (progressive feeding) in contrast to the mass provisioning practised by solitary bees. After 13 days as pupae the soft downy adults emerge. Hence there are altogether 21 days from egg to adult. The larval and pupal stages of the drone are slightly longer making a total of 24 days. Apart from their larger size drone cells can be easily recognized during the pupal stage by their much more pronounced concave wax capping.

Drones are large and stocky with blunt abdomens. At first they are fed by the workers but after about a week they are able to feed themselves from the honey stores of the colony. They are not usually produced until late spring. Their sole function is to fertilize any young queen and to help them achieve this they have powerful thoracic flight muscles and large eyes. In warm afternoons

Sealed honeybee queen cell, from side.

Honeybee pupae, each in its separate cell in the comb.

they congregate and patrol in special areas, 30–50 ft (9–15 m) above ground, to which the queens are attracted and where mating occurs. The highly specialized genital apparatus of the drones includes an enormously developed penis which is torn from its base when it is everted into the vagina of the queen and in the process of copulation the drone dies. However, although every queen mates more than once, only comparatively few drones can participate in the act and when the summer's end is approaching and the useful-

ness of drones is at an end, they are left in a corner of the hive, starved of food and eventually dragged from the hive entrance.

New queens are reared in special cells that hang vertically downward from the comb. The queen larvae receive special food and attention and their total period of development is only 16 days. They are either reared to replace the queen of the colony when she is dead or failing, or because the colony is about to reproduce by swarming and a new queen is needed to replace the mother queen which will leave with the swarm. Bees that leave with the swarm each carry a supply of honey in their honeystomachs and as soon as the swarm has settled in its new home some of this is rapidly converted into wax to start building the new comb.

Although we are now familiar with the life-histories of many of our solitary and social bees, and with the activities of the individuals, we still have a great deal to learn about why or how they perform these activities. In particular the ways in which the activities of the thousands of individuals comprising a honeybee colony, are co-ordinated in relation to the needs of the colony are only just beginning to be understood. Foraging is the bees' most important activity as far as man is concerned. Since primitive times man has robbed wild colonies of their stores of honey and for many centuries honeybee colonies have been kept in various straw baskets and wooden boxes known as hives, for the sole purpose of collecting a harvest of honey at the end of the season. The methods of bee-keeping have been improved consistently over the years but the greatest advance came when the Rev L. L. Langstroth invented a hive with movable combs, so that the activities of the bees could be determined at any time, and if necessary

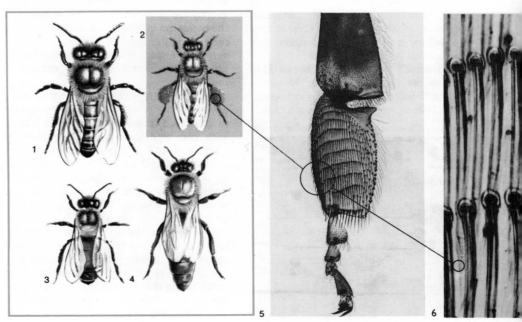

The honeybees and the way workers carry pollen. 1. and; 2. worker bee with mass of pollen on each hindleg; 3. drone; 4. queen; 5. part of hindleg, enlarged 26 times, showing hairs and 'basket' in which pollen is carried; 6. part of 'basket', enlarged 165 times; the cells holding pollen are now clearly visible.

appropriate measures taken by the beekeeper.

Although of great importance economically in many parts of the world, especially in North America and Australia, the honeybee performs its greatest service to man by pollinating flowers while visiting them to collect nectar and pollen. Indeed many of our crops, such as tree fruits, red clover and runner beans, are entirely dependent on insect pollination to produce fruit or seed. Others, such as blackcurrants, mustard and field beans, produce more abundant crops following pollination. Insect pollination often also has the effect of producing larger and better quality fruits. It is impossible to evaluate accurately the services of bees to agriculture and horticulture, but all authorities agree that their pollinating activities are of far greater value than any honey produced.

Attempts are also being made to use bumblebees to pollinate some of our crops, particularly red clover and lucerne. At various research stations throughout the world queen bumblebees have been induced to start their colonies in captivity in the laboratory or in specially prepared domiciles in the field, the colonies then formed being transported to sites where they are needed. However, there is much to learn before bumblebees can be used on an economic scale.

Solitary bees are already being used commercially for pollinating lucerne, chiefly in the United States and Canada, and to a small extent in a few other countries. For example, the solitary bee, *Nomia melanderi,* which was previously restricted by the specific requirements of its nesting site has been induced in recent years to nest in special artificial nest beds with soil of the correct texture, alkalinity and moisture content prepared in the vicinity of lucerne fields, with notable success. Another bee being used, *Megachile rotundata,* nests in tunnels above ground and special shelters containing thousands of straws, or wooden tunnels provided for it to nest in, are distributed in lucerne fields needing pollination.

Undoubtedly we are only just beginning to make proper use of pollinating bees. The potential is enormous. ORDER: Hymenoptera, CLASS: Insecta, PHYLUM: Arthropoda. J.B.F.

Holes bored in wood by Carpenter bee *Osmia rufa.*

BEES IN A RIDDLE. From earliest times it was thought possible to obtain a swarm of honeybees by killing an ox and leaving it to rot. This idea of 'spontaneous generation' of animals from dead material was not finally disproved until Louis Pasteur carried out his classical experiments. Yet there is an explanation to the story, because a species of Hover fly lays its eggs in rotten carcases. This is the Drone fly *Eristalis tenax* which is so called because it too looks very much like the drone, or male honeybee. It was large numbers of Drone flies emerging from the carcase that gave the impression of a swarm of bees. It is likely that Drone flies are the true answer to Samson's riddle of 'out of the strong came forth sweetness', alluding to the bees in the carcase of the lion he had previously slain.

BEE-EATERS, a family of insect-eating, bright-plumaged attractive birds of the Old World; chiefly found in the tropics, with one species in Europe and one in Australia. They live on flying insects, caught in graceful pursuit flights, and have pointed, rather long decurved beaks, pointed wings and very short legs. The sexes are similar. In some species the central tail feathers are elongated.

Bee-eaters comprise a uniform group, and the 24 species are currently placed in three genera of which the most important is *Merops,* with 21 species. The family Meropidae is classified in the order Coraciiformes, and although it is not particularly closely related to the other families—kingfishers, rollers, hoopoes, hornbills etc., all of them share certain behavioural characteristics (e.g. hole-nesting) and structural ones. In the American tropics, an unrelated family in another order, the jacamars (Galbulidae) fills exactly the same 'niche' or place in nature as the bee-eaters in Africa and Asia, and during their evolution the two families have converged in respect of diet and feeding habits, plumage, size, breeding biology and behaviour.

Bee-eaters are well named, for practically all the species which have been investigated in detail feed exclusively on airborne insects, with bees and their allies (Hymenoptera) comprising 80% or more of their diet. There are two principal ways of feeding; the smaller species keep watch for passing insects from a vantage-point like a bush, fence-post or telephone wire, and the larger species hunt on the wing. In either case an insect is pursued with a fast and dextrous flight and snapped up in the bill. Generally the bird returns to its perch, where it beats the prey against the perch until it is inactive. Over much of the range of the family, the various bee-eaters subsist largely on honeybees. The venomous workers of honeybees and

other stinging Hymenoptera have their stings removed by an instinctive pattern of behaviour, improved by the fledgling bee-eater with experience. The insect is held in the beak near the tip of its abdomen, which is rubbed against the perch so that the venom is discharged. Apart from bees, most other suitably-sized flying insects are also preyed upon: demoiselle-flies, termites, butterflies, bugs, beetles, grasshoppers etc. After a rainstorm in Africa, flying ants and termites emerge in great profusion and are hunted by many kinds of birds; an excited flock of wheeling bee-eaters is often in attendance.

The best known species is the European bee-eater *Merops apiaster.* It is a summer visitor to the Mediterranean countries, and western Asia, being found north of the Pyrenees, the Camargue, the Alps and Carpathians, 500 miles (800 km) north of the Black and Caspian Seas and east to Kash-

Carmine bee-eater *Merops nubicus.*

mir. It spends the winter in Africa south of the Sahara, particularly in southern Africa. Populations also winter in southwest Arabia and in northwest India. For many years now, small isolated colonies are known to have nested in a few localities in the Union of South Africa during the southern summer. This population is surely derived originally from migrant European bee-eaters, but it is not known whether, after nesting in South Africa, the same birds accompany other wintering bee-eaters back to Europe and Asia to nest again there six months later. Several other European bird visitors to temperate South Africa, like swallows *Hirundo rustica,* are known to nest there occasionally, but it seems unlikely that the self-same individuals breed again in Europe.

One of the gems of the European bird world, the beauty of the 11 in (27 cm) bee-eater has been extolled by travellers and naturalists alike. Its cinnamon crown and shoulders, gold scapulars, blue-green wings, green tail, black eye-stripe, yellow throat and apple-green underparts command attention as much as its confiding gregariousness and liquid trilling 'pruik' call-note. Like other bee-eater species, it prefers open countryside and the vicinity of water, and breeds in colonies of a few to a hundred or more pairs, in holes excavated in sandcliffs or flat ground. Occasionally European bee-eaters nest north of their usual range, in Germany and Denmark, and in 1955 three pairs nested in southern England, two successfully. Only once before this had a pair nested in Britain, but in most years there are a few records from Britain of vagrant bee-eaters in late summer and autumn.

All remaining members of the genus *Merops* have equally bright plumage, chiefly of greens, blues and yellows, hence the common name rainbow-bird for the Australian *M. ornatus*. All possess a black mask across the eyes, sometimes accentuated by a narrow pale blue or yellow line above and below it, and the chin and throat of most species are bright yellow or scarlet, contrasting with the surrounding plumage and delineated by a narrow black breast band. The West African Rosy bee-eater *M. malimbicus* is slaty black with a white moustache and pink underparts and Carmine bee-eaters *M. nubicus* of Africa are entirely carmine except for their blue heads. The latter is widespread throughout the savannahs of Africa. As it is the largest bee-eater in that continent and breeds in colonies sometimes of thousands, it is the most spectacular of all.

From southwest India to Indo-China and Borneo the genus *Nyctyornis* is found comprising two species of very large bee-eaters with rather stout beaks and living in forests. They take a generalized diet of insects, spiders and woodlice, but will catch some insects in flight, including bees. The plumage is princi-

Red-throated bee-eater *Merops bulocki*.

pally green; the throat and breast feathers are elongated and pendent, blue in the Indian *N. athertoni* and scarlet in the Malayan *N. amicta*. Another forest bee-eater, *Meropogon forsteni*, the affinities of which, within the family, are not understood, lives in Celebes and somewhat resembles three dark-plumaged forest species of western and central Africa. Less is known about these forest forms than about the open-country and savannah bee-eaters, but they seem to be less specialized in some respects.

The breeding biology of all bee-eaters seems to be very similar. Migrants start to excavate their nesting holes in sand banks or earth cliffs as soon as they arrive at their summer quarters, but sedentary species like the Red-throated bee-eater *Merops bulocki* of Africa, which breed at the end of the dry season when the gound is rock-hard, dig their nest holes in softer earth at the end of the previous rainy season, months in advance. In some species the tunnels are up to 8 ft (2·5 m) long, straight or a little angled, and they end in an oval chamber 6–10 in (15–25 cm) long. Here the two to six spherical white eggs are laid, without benefit of nesting material other than a thick carpet of the indigestible hard parts of insects, regurgitated in the chamber by adult birds and trodden underfoot into a crumbly mass smelling strongly of ammonia.

The young hatch naked and blind, but long before their eyes open at ten days they have learned to shuffle quickly on their swollen horny 'heel' pads when they hear a parent alight at the tunnel entrance with a meal. Fledging occurs after four weeks in the nest and for several more weeks the young birds are tended and fed, not only by their parents, but by other non-breeding adults as well. Juvenile plumage is identical with that of the adults. The hole-nesting habit does not ensure successful fledging, for parasitic honeyguides, egg-eating snakes and other predators enter and destroy the eggs; nests in flat ground may be flooded or covered by blown sand; and worst of all, cliffs may be so riddled with nest holes that they collapse.

Several species are trans-continental migrants. Large green bee-eaters from India, *Merops philippinus*, winter in the East Indies, and those from West Pakistan and trans-Caucasia, *M. superciliosus*, migrate to Africa as do the European bee-eaters. Rainbow-birds fly to New Guinea after breeding in Australia and most of the African species migrate regularly within that continent. It was doubtless disorientation on its spring passage that carried a vagrant Blue-cheeked bee-eater, a race of the Large green bee-eater which breeds in the Middle East, to southwest England in 1951, giving rise to the only European record north of the Mediterranean.

In Africa, Carmine bee-eaters extend their north tropical and south tropical ranges towards the Equator after their respective breeding seasons, but this is more in the nature of vagrancy than regular migration. Although it eats bees wherever they can be readily caught, this species is really a hunter of grasshoppers and locusts, and its vagrancy in the savannahs is doubtless related to that of its locust prey. Carmine bee-eaters are always attracted to bush-fires and circle about snapping up fleeing grasshoppers and for this reason, as well as for their magnificent plumage they have a good claim to the name 'fire-bird'. Also connected with its predilection for grasshoppers is the Carmine bee-eater's strange habit of consorting with and riding upon larger animals

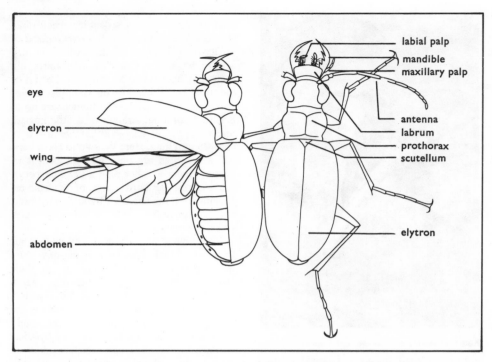

The morphology of a typical beetle. On the left the insect is shown with one of the elytra raised, as in flight, exposing the wing.

moving through savannah grassland—cattle, antelopes, ostriches and even bustards serve as convenient vehicles.

Another curious feeding association concerns the White-throated bee-eater *M. albicollis*. In southern Nigeria, fragments of the highly nutritious skin of Oil-palm fruits were found in the birds' gizzards. How they got there was not understood until close observation revealed that small squirrels, hidden in the heads of the palm trees, were stripping the fruits; any pieces that they dropped were skillfully caught by attendant bee-eaters before they reached the ground. It is possible that White-throated bee-eaters turn to an oil-rich diet at that season, just before the 1,000 mile (1,600 km) migration from the forest-edge to breeding quarters at the edge of the Sahara, so enabling them to lay down fat as fuel for the journey. FAMILY: Meropidae, ORDER: Coraciiformes, CLASS: Aves.   C.H.F.

BEETLE, common name for all insects of the order Coleoptera (=sheath wings), which have the first pair of wings modified to form wingcases (elytra); these nearly always meet in a straight line down the middle of the back. In addition, beetles normally have biting mouthparts which project forwards and a life-history with larval and pupal stages. Cockroaches are often wrongly thought to be beetles.

They are the largest order of animals with nearly 300,000 species so far described. In body size they cover most of the insect range. The shortest and lightest are Feather-wing beetles (Ptiliidae) which are less than $\frac{1}{60}$ in

Female Stag beetle *Lucanus cervus* lacks 'antlers'. Below: the male Stag beetle with large 'antlers'.

Male Hercules beetle *Dynastes hercules*, Colombia.

(0·04 cm) long. The heaviest are Goliath, Elephant and Hercules beetles (Scarabaeidae). Both Hercules beetles and some Timber beetles (Cerambycidae) reach $6\frac{1}{4}$ in (16 cm), and it is stated that some Timber beetles (e.g. *Titanus giganteus*) may reach a length of 8 in (20 cm). Beetles also have a great diversity of forms and colours, ranging from dull, black Ground beetles to brilliant, metallic Jewel beetles (Buprestidae) and Diamond beetles (Curculionidae). Both shape and colour are due to the outer covering, or cuticle. Since this is often very hard, beetles are tough enough to survive accidents or attacks which would disable other insects. Indeed, the Coleoptera are the most obviously armoured order of an armoured class.

Structure. The biting mouthparts consist of strong mandibles covered by the flap of the labrum (upper lip), and rake- or brush-like maxillae (second jaws) which move the food back to the mouth over the tray-like labium (lower lip). Behind this is the gula, a throat region characteristic of beetles. The mouthparts are modified in some beetles for piercing and sucking, or even for lapping up fluids. Palps on the maxillae and labium are organs of touch and taste. The antennae (for touch and smell) usually have 11 segments and range from thread-like or comb-like to a variety of club shapes. The eyes are large in daytime predators, but are small or absent in some cave species and in many larvae.

Seen from above, the prothorax is a large, mobile segment lying between head and hindbody. The latter consists of the second and third thoracic segments and abdomen all covered by the elytra, although the end of the abdomen may project slightly. In Rove beetles (Staphylinidae), several segments of the very mobile abdomen project. The elytra, which are often grooved and closely fitted, protect the delicate hindwings. They are secured by a tiny, triangular catch—the scutellum. When this is moved forwards, the elytra can be raised and the wings unfolded. Strong fliers such as chafers and Timber beetles may travel great distances, but most beetles are less accomplished fliers and some Ground beetles and weevils have become flightless.

Beetles usually live either on the surface of the soil and vegetation, or just beneath it and their habits are most clearly expressed in their leg structure. Active runners (e.g. Ground beetles) have long, slender legs whilst in climbing species such as Leaf beetles and weevils the tarsi (feet) are broad and carry pads of adhesive hairs. In Flea beetles (Chrysomelidae) and some weevils the hind-legs are enlarged for jumping, whilst in many burrowers the front legs are expanded and spiny. Most water beetles have the middle and hindlegs flattened and hair-fringed for swimming and in the Whirligig beetles these legs from short, broad paddles for surface skating.

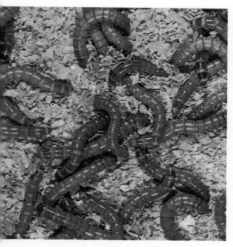

Mealworms, the larvae of a beetle *Tenebrio molitor*, a pest of the flour mills, which has become well-known through being widely used to feed caged birds and other pets.

Classification. There are two large and two small suborders of Coleoptera. 1 Archostemata includes the most primitive living beetles (Cupedidae) which were the dominant beetles in the Permian period, 200 million years ago. 2 Adephaga is the second largest suborder with about 12 families of mainly carnivorous land and water beetles. Ground beetles (Carabidae) form the largest family. The

water beetles include Diving beetles (Dytiscidae) and Whirligig beetles (Gyrinidae). 3 Polyphaga is much the largest suborder with about 130 families containing 90% of all beetles. Major families are weevils and Bark beetles (Curculionidae, the largest animal family), Leaf beetles (Chrysomelidae), Timber beetles (Cerambycidae), Rove beetles (Staphylinidae), Dung beetles and chafers (Scarabaeidae), Jewel beetles (Buprestidae), Mealworm beetles (Tenebrionidae), Click beetles (Elateridae) and ladybirds (Coccinellidae). 4 Myxophaga has only a few small families.

Distribution. Beetles are the most widely distributed order both on land and in fresh-

A blue *Eupholus* weevil of New Guinea.

Goliath beetle *Goliathus giganteus*, one of the largest beetles.

water. They are found almost everywhere except in the sea. The more unusual habitats include deserts (especially Tenebrionidae), caves, sea-shores, all kinds of fresh water (several families), the nests of birds, termites and ants (there are many ways to fit into ant societies) and most of man's stored products. Some of the largest families (e.g. weevils and Ground beetles) have a world-wide distribution whilst other families are more restricted. For instance, the carnivorous Diving beetles are found mainly in the northern hemisphere whilst Jewel beetles are a mainly

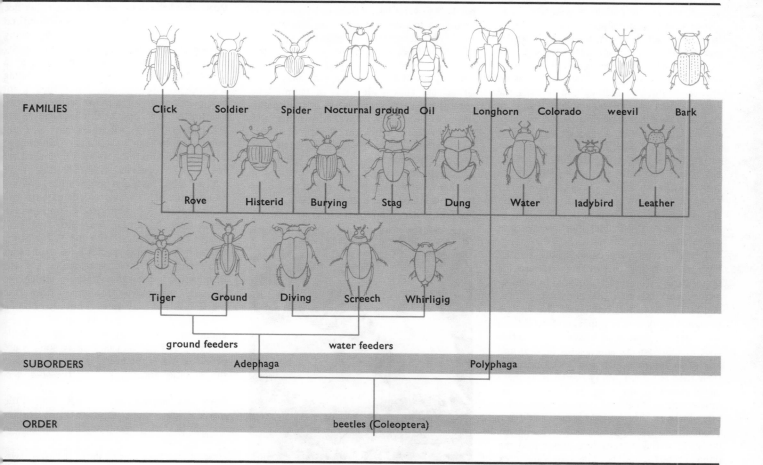

Weevil *Eupholus hickleri* of New Guinea, from the Hertzog Mountains, Vagau.

tropical group. Many species are restricted to small areas, but over 100 kinds of beetles are now cosmopolitan, having been distributed around the world by man.

Breeding and life history. Although it is often difficult to distinguish between the sexes, in some beetles the male has greatly enlarged jaws (Stag beetles) or horns (Hercules beetles) and in others the female is wingless, as in glow-worms. The female glow-worm uses light to attract the male, while other beetles use special scents (e.g. Bark beetles). The courtship which follows is usually a simple process, as is egg-laying. The female has no special ovipositor, although in weevils the snout is often used to drill a hole. The smooth eggs are laid either at random or in a prepared niche. Occasionally, a special egg-case is made, like the floating silk cocoon of vegetarian Water beetles (Hydrophilidae). If the egg is not laid near the larval food, a food store may be added (e.g. Dung beetles). Some Dung beetles show a degree of parental care rare in beetles although it is also found in Sexton beetles (Silphidae), Bark beetles and Passalidae.

Beetle larvae vary considerably but all have either biting or piercing and sucking mouthparts. The head capsule is usually harder than the rest of the body, which may end in a pair of short processes. The legs are large and spiny in active species (Ground and Rove beetles), smaller or weaker in less active species (wireworms and chafer larvae) and absent in larvae which live surrounded by their food (weevils). Many beetles have three larval stages but there may be 12 or more, as in wireworms. The pupa is usually concealed often in an earthen cell and occasionally in a cocoon, and the appendages lie free on the body. In a few beetles (e.g. ladybirds) the pupa is exposed and the appendages are stuck

to the body. The strangest life-histories are of those species in which an active first stage larva is succeeded by semi-parasitic larvae, as in Blister beetles (Meloidae) with locust hosts. The most specialized are *Stylops* in which the male is free-living and the female is a larva-like parasite. (They are often put in a separate order, the Strepsiptera). The length of beetle life-cycles varies from only one or two weeks up to over five years. In one case, a Timber beetle in a very dry pine-wood pillar is known to have emerged 45 years after the wood was felled.

Feeding. Beetles, and more especially their larvae, eat almost all kinds of animal and vegetable materials, and even some inorganic ones. The majority are herbivorous and include weevils, which eat all parts of plants, and Leaf beetles which feed mainly on the soft tissues. Plant-feeders are usually specialists and may eat only a particular part at a particular time. Tree-trunks are tunnelled by larvae of Timber and Bark beetles, while roots

Pupae of Violet ground beetle.

are eaten by wireworms and chafer larvae. Some large beetles will only take nectar whilst many small species thrive on fungi. Most of the Adephaga are carnivorous and include voracious hunters such as Tiger beetles (Cicindelidae) and the large Diving beetles ('water tigers'). Many predators have specialized on certain prey species, for instance, in the Polyphaga, ladybirds eat mainly aphids and Scale insects whilst Chequered beetles (Cleridae) hunt for Bark beetles.

There are few parasitic beetles, but these include both external parasites (e.g. Leptinidae, including a beaver parasite) and internal ones (e.g. Rhipiphoridae, including a wasp parasite). Scavenging is far commoner amongst beetles, particularly in substances like dung and carrion which are always available. Dung beetles like the Dor beetle (Geotrupidae) tunnel in and under cowpats, although some large species such as the Sacred beetle will roll away a ball of dung to consume at leisure. Decaying carcasses have a succession of beetles of which a few are carrion-eaters (e.g. some Silphidae) but the majority are predators of maggots, etc. However, drying carcasses provide food for skin and bone specialists (e.g. Dermestidae). The Burying (or Sexton) beetles *Necrophorus* are particularly interesting as a pair can bury a whole dead rat or small bird to provide food for themselves and their young.

Protective behaviour. Most beetles either flee or 'freeze' before a predator. Thus Ground and Rove beetles can usually run rapidly, many beetles can fly and some can jump either by using enlarged hindlegs (Flea beetles) or, as in Click beetles, by jack-knifing and bouncing themselves into the air. Threatened plant beetles often drop and freeze so they may be overlooked. The best at this manoeuvre are Pill beetles (Byrrhidae) where both legs and antennae fold flush into grooves. Camouflage can also aid obscurity, as seen in green Leaf beetles and weevils. Some beetles have evolved a bad taste and have warning colours to advertise it; ladybird colour-patterns are examples of this. Conversely, unprotected beetles may mimic species which have protection as is the case with the Wasp beetle *Clytus arietis*. Some species have unpleasant secretions. The most spectacular are the Bombadier beetles *Brachinus* in which the accurate explosive discharge from the hindend is not only smelly, but also boiling hot. Many adults and larvae can make sounds, not explosively but with a cuticular file and rasper. In some cases, these sounds are produced when the beetle is disturbed, as in the aquatic Screech beetle *Hygrobia hermanni*.

Economic importance. Beetles have little medical importance although some species contain blistering agents such as cantharidin

Head of Stag beetle larva, showing strong jaws.

(in Blister beetles (Meloidae) e.g. Spanish fly *Lytta vesicatoria*) and paederin (some Staphylinidae). Also, some small Indian Dung beetles are a rare cause of diarrhoea. The economically important beetles are pests of agriculture, timber and stored products. A great many Leaf beetles, weevils, wireworms and chafer larvae attack crops. For instance, the Colorado beetle *Leptinotarsa decemlineata* is a Leaf beetle that attacks potatoes. It spread rapidly across Europe after its introduction from North America in 1922, but so far it has been controlled in Britain. There it is the only beetle notifiable to the police. Timber is tunnelled at all stages from forest to furniture by Timber beetles, weevils, Bark beetles and Furniture beetles (e.g. woodworm and Death watch beetle). A serious side effect of many crop- and timber-feeders is the transfer of fungal or viral diseases from plant to plant. Stored foods may be infested by mealworm and Flour beetles (Tenebrionidae) and Grain weevils, but other materials ranging from museum specimens to lead cable sheaths may be subject to beetle attacks. Not all beetles are pests, however, for many (including Ground beetles, Rove beetles and ladybirds) are beneficial predators. In fact, the first successful biological control of a pest was through the introduction into California of an Australian ladybird, *Rodolia cardinalis*, which controlled an epidemic of citrus Scale insects in 1888–90. ORDER: Coleoptera, CLASS: Insecta, PHYLUM: Arthropoda.

M.E.G.E.

BEHAVIOUR, mainly the response to the stimuli an animal receives from its environment. Some behaviour, however, seems to be the spontaneous result of internal factors. This is particularly true of *rhythmic behaviour which continues even in the absence of rhythmic environmental stimuli. Sensitivity to stimuli rests upon what was once called the 'irritability' of protoplasm. This is still a useful general concept, its physiological basis having now been shown to lie in changes in the electrical properties of cell membranes, as exemplified by those accompanying a nerve impulse.

The sensory abilities of an animal clearly determine the stimuli to which it can react. Some Cave fish are blind; while being generally sensitive to light and dark they cannot respond to shapes. Elasmobranch fish may respond to low-pitched sounds but they do not have the sensory apparatus to detect higher pitched noises. Similarly the response which an animal gives depends upon its motor equipment. Fish, for example, cannot grasp an object but an octopus can; the lack of ability to manipulate materials reduces the possibility of a fish making an elaborate nest like those of some birds, though some fishes do make crude nests. Birds, on the other hand, have their forelimbs completely converted for flight but have considerable manipulative ability by using a combination of beak and hind feet.

We can ask a number of questions when we observe a pattern of behaviour in an animal. First, what is its purpose? This is aimed at exploring its biological fitness in the life of the animal. The pattern may be one which permits it to find food and consume it, or to find a mate and reproduce the species. But there are also some forms of behaviour which are not related to feeding or reproduction. These, such as grooming behaviour, are classed as maintenance behaviour. By means of these responses an animal stays alive. Thus, a locust turns its body side-on to the sun's rays in the morning, thus heating up its body in readiness for active movement. As the sun rises higher and its body temperature reaches the necessary limits it turns head-on to the sun, reducing the area directly exposed and thus decreasing the heating effect of the sun's rays.

A second question is how did the behaviour come about? This is aimed at revealing the causation of the behaviour. For this purpose it is necessary to analyse most carefully the stimuli which the animal is receiving. It is easy to be deceived into believing the animal is reacting to stimuli, which it is, in fact, ignoring. A well known example of such deception is that of the horse called Clever Hans. This horse appeared to be able to work out simple sums written up on a blackboard. It pawed the ground with a front hoof as many times as was necessary to give the correct answer. This mysterious and totally unexpected mathematical ability was explained when all onlookers left him. He then went on scraping the floor without ceasing. The horse had been picking up clues as to when to stop scraping from the reaction of his trainer and other bystanders.

A third question is where did the behaviour come from? For all behaviour, just as all morphological characters, has an evolutionary history. It has developed and been selected by the process of natural selection which operates on all characteristics of living things. Comparison of behaviour patterns of the nearly related species shows the direction in which the process has gone. The behaviour of kittiwakes has been shown, for example, to have arisen from patterns of behaviour common to many gulls, but which have become modified in respect of their cliff-nesting habits.

While the answering of this third question may indicate the history of the behaviour, it does not necessarily tell us what determined it in the particular animal we are studying. To do this we must ask a fourth question, how did this behaviour pattern develop? We need to know when in the animal's life it appeared and whether there was any preceding behaviour which was a necessary precursor, or any special experience which the animal had undergone. This information enables us to judge the extent to which inherited factors are responsible for the pattern and how far experience has moulded it. Behaviour ranges from that which is largely determined genetically—like much species-specific behaviour, to that which is largely acquired such as—learned behaviour (see heredity and environment).

It is in such species-specific behaviour we find the greatest influence on evolution for it is a potent agent in the origin of the species. Many authorities believe that geographical isolation of part of the population is essential for the separation of the population into two species. One of the differences which may arise during this isolation is changes in the species-specific signals by which one individual attracts another for mating. Should the isolated parts of the population once again make contact with one another, the reproductive isolation may be maintained by these behavioural differences. Species differentiation would then have resulted.

In general terms, the complexity and adaptability of behaviour correlates with the elaboration of the nervous system. Higher types of learning are found in mammals with full development of the cerebral cortex. On the other hand, learning is not by any means absent from the social insects. It is difficult to grade behaviour patterns according to complexity, for even the apparently simple orientation behaviour of some invertebrates, such as the movement of a flatworm towards its food, necessitates a degree of co-ordination of muscular contraction throughout the body. It would also be a mistake to think that all the behaviour of higher animals is complex, there is much that is of the simplest kind. To take an extreme, man has a knee-jerk reflex which involves the spinal cord alone and requires no reference to his highly developed brain.

J.D.C.

BEHAVIOURISM, one of the characteristics which distinguishes man from the rest of the animals is his ability to look at himself and consider his own motivation. This power of introspection is the basis upon which the science of psychology was established. When we think about human behaviour we make the implicit assumption that other people's minds are like our own and that therefore, we can examine our own thoughts as a model of what is general to all human thought. No examination of animal behaviour in this way is possible; we cannot gain an insight into the animal mind and the imputation of human motives and feelings to animals is not without its dangers (see anthropomorphism).

Central to much of psychologists' thought in the last century was the concept of 'mind' but the work of Pavlov on *conditioned

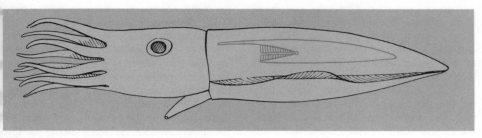

Reconstruction of a belemnite, showing the supposed relationship of the soft parts to the skeleton (blue) the only part of which fossil remains are known.

reflexes led some workers, particularly in the USA, to doubt whether mind was a necessary part of human behaviour. It was J. B. Watson who led this revolt against introspective psychology, publishing *Psychology from the Standpoint of a Behaviourist* in 1919. He proposed to view all behaviour as based on the traditional reflex arc and thus his school was accused of 'stimulus-response'. Learning wherever it could be proved in living things was thought to be derived from conditioning of the Pavlovian type. This school was more properly called Behaviourist. Watson advocated, in particular, the study of sensory perception by means of conditioning. This was a swing from a vitalist view of living things towards a more mechanistic one and was in a sense typical of the time. Jacques Loeb had approached embryology and the simpler behaviour patterns of insects in this way. His belief was that all living processes could be explained in terms of physics and chemistry. Thus, if an insect, illuminated from one side, turned towards the source of the light, it was due to a more or less direct effect of light stimulation on the muscles of that side, preventing them from moving the legs in strides as long as those on the other side.

Behaviourism had a particularly profound effect on psychology in the USA where it stimulated a healthily critical biological approach to the study of behaviour, seen most especially in the initiation of studies of the genetics of behaviour and comparative behaviour. It took psychology into the laboratory where traditional experimental method would be used and established the study of learning in the central position it occupies in America today.

Now the approach is echoed in N. Tinbergen's call for an objectivistic approach to the study of animals in the wild. The need for description which can be free of the interjection of human value judgements and of anthropomorphism is very great especially when comparative study of species patterns is being attempted. However, there is no doubt today that whether we term it 'mind' or not, what are called the higher activities of the central nervous system cannot really be ignored.   J.D.C.

BEIRA *Dorcatrogus megalotis,* of Somalia, one of the *Dwarf antelopes.

BELEMNITES, extinct cephalopod molluscs closely related to living octopuses, squids and cuttlefishes. They were all marine and probably arose from primitive nautiloids with straight, external shells at least as early as the Devonian Period, 350–400 million years ago. The walls of the shell gradually became enormously thickened and grew backward to form the guard while the phragmocone and body chamber decreased in size. At the same time the soft parts spread backwards and upwards to surround the shell. These changes resulted in a considerable improvement in streamlining but adversely affected the buoyancy. Even if the reduced phragmocone was capable of being filled with gas it could not compensate for the increase in weight due to the heavy guard, and the animals must have been significantly heavier than sea water. They were probably swift but inefficient swimmers.

The earliest belemnites known are from the Carboniferous. They were common during the Jurassic and Cretaceous Periods and occur in great numbers in certain formations. They died out in the Eocene. Most fossils consist of only the guard though specimens showing part of the phragmocone are not uncommon. Because of their shape they are sometimes known as thunderbolts.

The shell of a belemnite consists of three parts: the guard or rostrum, the phragmocone and the pro-ostracum. The guard is very strong and forms most of the skeleton. It is roughly cigar-shaped and tapers to a point posteriorly. There is a funnel-shaped cavity, the alveolus, in front, but apart from this the guard is solid and consists of crystals of calcite, a form of calcium carbonate, radiating outwards from its long axis. The phragmocone lies within the alveolus. It corresponds to the chambered part of the shell of the Pearly nautilus but is very much reduced. Its cavity is divided by closely spaced, transverse septa; these are slightly curved with the concavity directed forwards and are attached to the thin wall of the phragmocone in simple circular sutures. There is a very slender siphuncular tube which presumably contained a siphon in life though this could have been little more than a vestige. The pro-ostracum is a shoehorn-shaped projection extending forwards from the dorsal edge of the alveolus. It protected the soft parts of the animal to some extent and probably represents the remains of the body chamber.

It is obvious that a shell of this nature could not possibly enclose the animal and this is confirmed by some unusually well-preserved fossils from the Jurassic lithographic limestone of Bavaria and from the Cretaceous limestones of the Lebanon. These show the squid-like shape of the animal, the internal shell, a small number of arms probably ten, an ink-sac and the horny jaws. The arms bore many small, chitinous hooks but no suckers. The number of gills is not known but there are good reasons for supposing that belemnites had only one pair.

In classifications catering mainly for living forms, and hence based chiefly on soft structures, the belemnites are included in the order Dibranchiata and suborder Decapoda. In the classification generally used by paleontologists the belemnites, as the order Belemnoidea, are placed in the subclass Coleoidea which contains all the cephalopods with a reduced, internal shell. PHYLUM: Mollusca.   Jo.G.

BELLBIRD, a name used in various countries for birds with bell-like calls. In South

Bearded bellbird *Procnias averano*, of South America and the island of Trinidad. The male has a metallic call which he makes from a fixed point throughout the day.

America it is used for several species of cotingas of the genus *Procnias* (Cotingidae). These are about the size of large thrushes and may have a featherless throat or various types of vermiform wattles. Their calls consist of far-carrying notes, like the tolling of a large bell or the clang of a hammer on an anvil, and may be monotonously repeated for long periods. These calls can be heard up to a mile away and may be intolerably loud at close quarters. The birds are forest-dwelling, fruit-eating species and little is known of their life-histories.

In Australia the name is applied to the Crested bellbird, *Oreoica guttaralis,* a species of whistler (Pachycephalinae). This is a bird of dry regions, thrush-like and dull brown in colour with a short erectile crest. The male has a mainly black head, and is white around the bill and throat. The bell-like call in this species consists of two slow notes followed by three quieter ones, all uttered in a muted ringing tone which makes the call sound like a distant cattlebell. It is ventriloquial in quality, the bird being difficult to locate from the sound which seems to come from much farther off. The bird usually feeds on the ground, hopping around and mainly taking insects. The cup-shaped nest, concealed in a bush or tree, is built of strips of bark with finer lining. This species has the odd habit of placing live, usually hairy, caterpillars, which have been apparently rendered torpid through squeezing, around the rim of the nest.

In New Zealand the name is used for a species of honey-eater, *Anthornis melanura,* Meliphagidae. This is again about the size of a thrush and a dull olive and yellowish green in colour, the male plumage having some iridescent purple on the head and yellow tufts at the sides of the breast. The song, which may be heard at all times of the year, is a series of up to six notes, of a liquid quality, and at a distance the louder notes sound remarkably bell-like. The female also sings, but her song is shorter and weaker. This species is a bird of the forest and forest-edge. In addition to nectar it also feeds on fruit and insects. It builds a cup-shaped nest in the fork of a tree, containing pink eggs with reddish spots. In Australia a related honey-eater, *Manorina melanophrys,* is called the Bell miner and is said to have a similar song resembling the tinkling of a silver bell.

BELUGA, derived from the Russian for 'white' is the name for two animals. The beluga *Huso huso* is the largest of the *sturgeons and probably the largest of all freshwater fishes. It is found in the seas and rivers of the Soviet Union and reaches 29 ft (8·8 m). The beluga *Delphinapterus leucas,* or *White whale, is a relative of the narwhal. It lives in northern seas, grows to 18 ft (5·5 m).

BENTHOS, the fauna of the sea floor. Benthic populations inhabit both the continental shelf, in which case they will be living on the bottom at a depth of about 650 ft (200 m), and also the floor of the oceans themselves, at an average depth of about 13,000 ft (4,000 m). Except in shallow regions of less than 330 ft (100 m) only the faintest light reaches the sea floor, so plants (algae) are rare. The communities of animals, however, are surprisingly rich and varied, their composition depending in the main on the nature of the bottom, the strength of the currents, the extent of turbidity, and similar factors. Environmental conditions in a given locality are generally much more constant than those experienced by inhabitants of the intertidal zone, for example, for there are rarely significant fluctuations in temperature and salinity.

Most of the sea floor is of soft mud and ooze, largely the result of material which, over the millennia, has drifted down from lesser depths. Many species burrow in these soft deposits—polychaetes, bivalve molluscs, Sea urchins and the like. Others, such as crabs, crawl over its surface, or, like the bottom-dwelling fishes, swim just above it. Where currents are strong, however, or the surface is too steep to retain sinking particles, the bottom may be hard. On such rocky areas of the sea floor live fixed forms such as sponges, anemones, barnacles and Sea squirts. Crawling among these sessile forms are found such animals as starfish and crabs. A few species, one or two of the polychaetes and bivalve molluscs, burrow into the rock, there enjoying some protection from predators.

In the soft deposits may be found bacteria, protozoans and other microscopic organisms. The bacteria can be important

initiators of benthic food chains, as algae are generally absent. The bacteria utilize particles of matter which sink down from the surface layers and also inorganic substances dissolved in the water around them. Those bacteria that live free in the water supply food for the *filter-feeders, and those among the ooze provide food for the animals which swallow the bottom deposits. Filter-feeding is common among the benthos, partly due to the generally high turbidity. Many of the bivalve molluscs, for example, feed in this way. Others suck up the surface deposits. In addition to the particle-feeders the benthos contains active predators, such as starfishes and bottom-dwelling fishes.

As many members of the benthos feed either on materials within the ooze or on particles drifting down, and do not move about a great deal in search of food, they are not particularly active animals. They are therefore unlikely to explore the surrounding regions as adults thereby colonizing suitable areas around them. Many, however, produce larvae which rise into the surface waters and there drift in the plankton wherever the currents take them. In time they sink and, if they encounter a suitable substratum, may settle there and metamorphose into young adults. The occurrence of a planktonic larva in the life-cycle represents a very widespread device among benthic species by which new areas of the sea floor are explored and colonized.   A.E.B.

BERGMANN'S RULE, propounded in 1847 by Carl Bergmann, states that the body size of birds and mammals increases with increasing latitude. Under identical conditions all warm-blooded animals lose equal amounts of heat per unit area of body surface. Therefore

Benthic fauna from mud 50 m deep. Included are a Heart urchin, Sea cucumbers and Bristle worms.

Benthic fauna on the seashore including Dog whelks, Edible mussels, Acorn barnacles, Beadlet anemones and Common limpets.

if an animal lives in a cold place it is to its advantage to have as small a surface area as possible in relation to bulk. Since, however, the volume and mass increase as the cube of the linear dimensions and the surface only as the square, the surface area does not increase as rapidly as the volume. So a larger body mass serves to conserve heat by reducing the relative surface from which heat loss can take place. Small animals in cold climates may be unable to take in enough food for maintenance of body temperature, since heat lost by radiation must be replaced by further heat generated by metabolism, which in turn causes an acceleration of digestion demanding a further intake of food. They are said then to suffer from 'cold starvation'. Consequently, animals living in cold climates tend to be large, Blue whales and Polar bears.

Few critical studies have been conducted to test the validity of this rule, but it is known that the Tasmanian races of the Duck-billed platypus *Ornithorhynchus anatinus,* Spiny ant-eater *Tachyglossus aculeatus* and Great grey kangaroo *Macropus giganteus fuliginosus* are larger than those found in Australia where the mean temperature on the south coast is 4°C higher than it is in Tasmania. Brown bears also, are generally larger the farther north they live.

It is unfortunate that textbooks have accepted *Allen's and Bergmann's thoughts as rules, because there are as many examples in apparent defiance of them as there are in support. For example, a complete size range is seen in the penguins, from the large Emperor penguin *Aptenodytes forsteri* of the Antarctic to the Galapagos penguin *Sphenis-*

cus mendiculus of equatorial latitudes. The Little blue penguin *Eudyptula minor* is found considerably further south than *S. mendiculus,* yet is much smaller. This may be an example of apparent defiance, since its small size may have been evolved not so much in relation to temperature as to its food. Allen's and Bergmann's Rules serve to illustrate how little we know about adaptation of animals to their environment.

BERNARD C., 1813–1878. French physiologist, who contributed more than anyone else to the development of experimental physiology. A considerable theoretician, his fame rests nevertheless on his practical reputation, which he established in the face of considerable personal privations. His major contributions come under three headings.

First, he demonstrated the part played by the pancreas in digestion. Second, he proved the ability of the liver to manufacture sugar. And third, he discovered the vasomotor nerves which control the diameter of the blood vessels to the skin and thus the amount of blood passing through them: the mechanism of blanching and blushing. He worked in many other fields, including toxicology, and although in poor health enjoyed an old age of honour and distinction.

BEZOAR *Capra hircus,* wild goat and the best source of the bezoar stone said to be an antidote to poison. The 'stone' is a concretion found in the stomach or intestines of some animals, especially ruminants, formed of animal matter laid down around some foreign substance. See bovidae.

BHARAL or Blue sheep *Pseudois nayaur,* the least known member of the goat-sheep tribe, is not a sheep, as its popular name and external appearance erroneously suggest, but a goat which has independently acquired many sheep-like characteristics. Attempts to hybridize it with sheep have failed. Bharal are found at higher altitudes from Kashmir to western Mongolia, frequenting the cold alpine zone above the timberline. This goat appears to be specialized as a grazer like all sheep. Three races, including a dwarf Chinese variety have been recognized.

The bharal is not a large animal, the males rarely exceeding 150 lb (68 kg) in live weight. The head and horns resemble those of Barbary sheep and urials, but there is no long hair on the cheeks, chin or neck. The horns are as large as those of the much larger Barbary sheep, reaching up to 31 in (88 cm) in length with a basal circumference of 13½ in (34 cm). The body is stocky and the legs are short. The ears are long, narrow and pointed and the tail is long and naked on its underside. There are no preorbital, inguinal or interdigital glands. These are typical goat features. The skull is similar to that of the Barbary sheep, but more massive. Like all sheep or goats, the bharal has only two teats.

This is a strikingly coloured little goat with white margins down hind and front legs, a white rump patch and belly, the latter bordered by a dark brown flank stripe. The front of the legs, as well as the nose, neck and chest are dark brown, or even blackish in old males. The body is brown-grey in autumn. The smooth horns tend to be dark olive in colour. As in Bighorn sheep or Alpine ibex, the males tend to darken with age and lose the white hair on the front legs. During winter the coat fades as it does in sheep or ibex, and may appear whitish in spring.

Like sheep, bharal are social animals. Male and female groups range apart except

Bichir *Polypterus ornatipinnis* of the Congo Basin, up to 37 cm long, characteristically supports itself on its fanlike pectoral fins, when resting.

in the rut which begins sometime in late October. The large horns and sturdy skulls suggest that bharal clash forcefully. Occasionally, they fight like goats. The gestation period has been suggested as lasting six months, which is probably correct. Twins are uncommon. The usual life expectancy of 12 to 15 years is similar to that of Bighorn sheep. FAMILY: Bovidae, ORDER: Artiodactyla, CLASS: Mammalia.   V.G.

BICHIRS *Polypterus,* a genus of primitive freshwater fishes of Africa comprising about ten species. The reedfish *Erpetoichthys* (formerly known as *Calamoichthys*) is the only near relative of the primitive bichirs. The name *Polypterus* signifies 'many fins', for when these fishes are alarmed or excited a row of 8–15 little finlets are erected along the back. These are not displayed during normal swimming. The body is covered by thick, rhombic scales of a type known as ganoid (with a covering of ganoine as in certain extinct forms). A pair of spiracles (the vestigial first gill slits in most bony fishes) are conspicuous. In the larvae there are leaf-like external gills such as are known in the South American and African (but not Australian) lungfishes and also in amphibians but in no other bony fishes. In some species of *Polyp-*

terus these gills later disappear. The intestine has a spiral valve which serves to increase the absorbent surface of the gut. This, too, is a primitive feature that is now found only in sharks and in such bony fishes as the sturgeons, lungfishes, the coelacanth and such fishes as the bowfin in the order Holostei. Bichirs can live out of water for a while breathing air into their lungs which are large but not quite so efficient as those of the lungfishes. The pectoral fins are constructed in a way similar to those of the coelacanth and its fossil relatives, that is to say with the finrays arising from a fleshy lobe. *Erpetoichthys* is basically similar to *Polypterus* but has a more eel-like body.

The bichirs are clearly very primitive fishes but their exact relationship to living and fossil forms has been disputed. In the last century it was thought that the bichirs were related to the lungfishes. In 1929 C. Tate Regan placed the bichirs in the subclass Palaeopterygii (ancient fins) of the order Cladista. The great Russian ichthyologist Leon Berg, 20 years later, decided that the bichirs were so remote from other fishes that they deserved to be in a subclass of their own, the Brachiopterygii (short fins), that is equivalent to the subclass of lungfishes (Dipnoi) and the subclass containing all the ray-finned fishes (Actinopterygii). (See also under fishes, classification). Currently, there is a school of thought that considers the aberrant bichirs to be descendants of the Crossopterygii, the order that includes the coelacanth. As sometimes happens with interesting forms, however, there are no fossils and the true relationships of the bichirs must await the discovery of some fossil link. FAMILY: Polypteridae, ORDER: Polypteriformes, CLASS: Pisces.

BIDDER'S ORGAN, an organ found in toads of the family Bufonidae sited between the fat body and the ovary or the testis. It is smaller in the female than in the male and in the females of some species it disappears as the ovaries reach maturity. The organ contains immature egg-cells and if the ovaries or testes are removed it can develop into a functional ovary on each side.

BIG-EYES, perch-like fishes of tropical and subtropical seas. They have rough-edged scales, which make the body coarse to the touch, the eyes are large and the mouth is directed upwards. Many of them are bright red in colour. They are bottom-living fishes usually found at depths of several hundred feet and the largest grow to about 2 ft (70 cm) in length. As might be suspected from the size of the eyes, they are nocturnal. *Priacanthus cruentatus,* a species known as aweoweo in Hawaii, is unusual in being a shallow water form found in water of less than 6 ft (2 m). Big-eyes are of little commercial importance except in parts of southeast Asia where they are considered a delicacy when dried and salted. FAMILY: Priacanthidae, ORDER: Perciformes, CLASS: Pisces.

BIG GAME HUNTING, the pursuit and killing for sport of 'large game' such as lion, tiger, leopard, zebra, antelope, bear, deer, and moose, all large enough to necessitate the use of a rifle if they are to be killed satisfactorily. 'Small game' are those wild animals which can be successfully killed by means of a shotgun.

The principal big game hunting areas of the world today are North America, central and southeast Asia, and east, central and southwest Africa. There are five generally recognised procedures. In open country the hunter approaches the animal upwind and undercover, a method called 'stalking'. 'Still stalking' is used in forest of shrub conditions, and the hunter merely proceeds quietly, ready to shoot on sight. For herd animals such as elephants, 'tracking' is often employed. Animals that frequent dense forest or jungle, often have to be disturbed and driven in the direction of the hunter; this method of 'beating' or 'driving' requires the assistance of men or dogs. Finally, if the hunter elects to wait by a trail, or by a bait, for the animals to pass, it is called 'sitting up'.

BIGHORN SHEEP, wild sheep of the mountains of western North America. See Sheep, mountain.

BIGSCALE FISHES, a descriptive common name for members of the family Melamphaeidae, a group of deep-sea fishes related to the beryciform fishes. About 20 species are known, all of them small. FAMILY: Melamphaeidae, ORDER: Beryciformes, CLASS: Pisces.

BILATERAL SYMMETRY, or symmetry about a single vertical plane running through the long axis of the body and dividing it into two nearly identical halves. The two halves are in fact almost the mirror image of each other. A dog, for example, is bilaterally symmetrical about a line drawn from the tip of its snout to the root of the tail.

BILHARZIASIS, disease caused by the Blood fluke *Schistosoma,* which is a parasitic flatworm. The disease is known as bilharziasis in Africa, and as schistosomiasis in the rest of the world. A Blood fluke differs from the rest of the flatworms because the sexes are separate throughout life and because the adults live in the blood system of the final host, man. There are many references to bilharziasis in Egyptian medical papyri dating from around 1,500 BC and calcified fluke eggs have been found in mummies over 3,000 years old.

It is estimated that today the parasite is carried by nearly 150 million people in the semi-tropical and tropical regions of the world. In Egypt alone there are over 9 million people infected, which is nearly 40% of the population, and in the rural areas where the disease is endemic, all may be infected.

The Blood fluke has a primitive nervous system and no blood system, but has a most intricate and highly specialized reproductive cycle in which a snail is the intermediate host and man the final host. A sexual multiplication of the larvae occurs in the snail, the worms attaining sexual maturity in man.

There are three species of flukes commonly parasitic in man. In Africa adult *Schistosoma haematobium* are found in the veins of the bladder wall. The eggs may rupture the thin walls of the blood vessels with their terminal spine and be voided, together with blood, in the urine, this haematuria being a characteristic symptom of this variety of the disease. The intermediate host of this Blood fluke is the freshwater planorbid snail *Bulinus.*

The other two species of fluke live in the small blood vessels of the intestine and the passage of eggs into the intestine may give rise to diarrhoea with blood and mucus.

Schistosoma mansoni is widespread in Africa, South America and the West Indies and the intermediate host is the freshwater disc-shaped pulmonate snail, *Biomphalaria* in Africa and *Australorbis* and *Tropicorbis* in the New World.

The third variety of the disease is caused by *Schistosoma japonicum* and is very common in Japan, the Philippines, China and Southeast Asia, the intermediate host being an amphibious operculate snail, *Oncomelania.*

The life-cycle of the three flukes is very similar. A ciliated larva or miracidium develops within the egg capsule, usually while it is passing through the body of the human host. On being voided with the faeces or urine, the egg must reach fresh water for further development. Once in water the larva wriggles around inside the egg capsule and eventually escapes through the ruptured membranes. The larva is attracted to light and swims to the upper water layers where the snail hosts are commonly found on vegetation.

If a suitable species of snail is found, the larva enters with a burrowing action, aided by the secretion of enzymes, and changes to a sac-like structure called a mother sporocyst, inside the snail. This commences the asexual phase of larval multiplication, for small groups of cells soon form daughter sporocysts, which break out of the mother cyst and migrate around the snail's body. Many of these enter the digestive gland or liver of the snail, where they themselves produce clusters of cells each of which becomes a fork-tailed cercaria. The cercariae escape from the sporocyst and eventually erupt from the snail's tissues and swim in the water. Like the miracidia, they have a limited food supply within them and die if a suitable host is not found within a few hours. If a suitable host (man) is found, the cercariae attach themselves to the skin with a sucker and bore into the tissues with the aid of enzymes, leaving the tail behind.

The young flukes now enter the host's blood system and pass to the liver where they become sexually mature. They then migrate to the blood vessels of the bladder or intestine where pairing takes place. The female is more slender than the male and comes to lie in a ventral fold of the male's body. She lays numerous eggs each of which produces a miracidium that is either male or female. Each in turn becomes a mother sporocyst which produces about 30 daughter sporocysts, each producing about 40 cercariae, so that every egg ultimately gives rise to about 1,200 cercariae.

Bilharziasis rarely kills the human host, but impairs vitality, the general lassitude having a marked effect on the host's capacity to work. The wasted work days sap the economic strength of many underdeveloped countries and, ironically, many technical developments such as irrigation schemes have served to enlarge the infected areas and the number of people reached by contaminated water.

Attempts to control the disease have been directed at various parts of the life-cycle of the fluke. Epidemiological surveys are being conducted together with mass treatment of infected people with drugs, at important centres of the disease. Health education methods are used together with public health schemes for the provision of safe drinking water and washing facilities and the installation of efficient sanitation, but are expensive long-term measures. Destruction of the snail intermediate hosts with molluscicides, such as copper sulphate and sodium pentachlorophenate, has proved effective in some areas. This is expensive since complete destruction of the snails is almost impossible to achieve and control requires rigid surveillance programmes. Research is being direc-

ted towards finding more efficient drugs, more effective molluscicides, the production of vaccines to confer immunity and into studying the ecology of the snail intermediate hosts. ORDER: Digenea, CLASS: Trematoda, PHYLUM: Platyhelminthes. N.V.W.

BILLFISHES, a term chiefly used in the United States for the swordfish and the sailfish but sometimes used for some of the marlins (in which the snout may also be extended into a 'bill').

BINTURONG *Arctictis binturong,* a relative of the Palm civets but unlike them in appearance. It is long-bodied with short legs, 2–2½ ft (60–76 cm) long with a bushy, slightly prehensile, tail slightly less than this. Its coat is shaggy, black with brown or grey on the tips of the hairs, with long black ear-tufts and with white on the ears, face and unusually long whiskers. The binturong is nocturnal and spends the day mainly curled

The slow-moving, fruit-eating binturong.

Diagram illustrating the life-cycle of the Blood fluke *Schistosoma mansoni,* a parasitic flatworm.

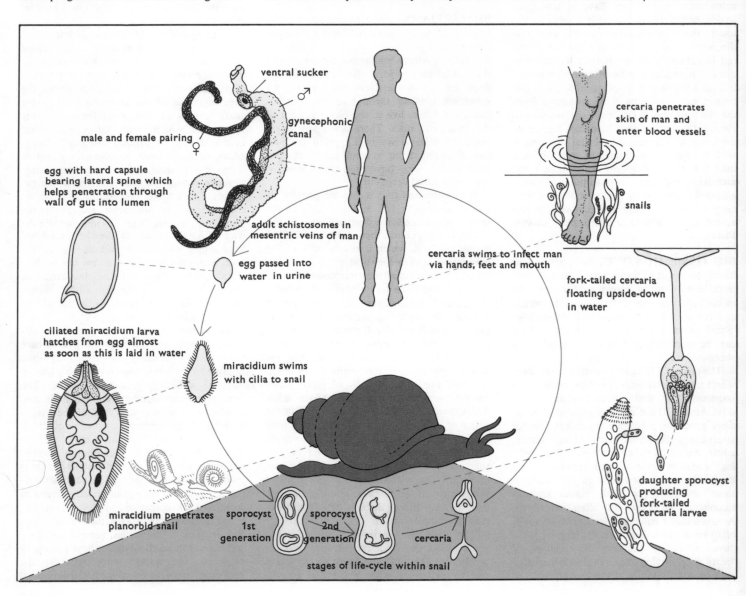

ventral sucker

male and female pairing

gynecephonic canal

egg with hard capsule bearing lateral spine which helps penetration through wall of gut into lumen

adult schistosomes in mesentric veins of man

egg passed into water in urine

ciliated miracidium larva hatches from egg almost as soon as this is laid in water

miracidium swims with cilia to snail

miracidium penetrates planorbid snail

sporocyst 1st generation

sporocyst 2nd generation

cercaria

stages of life-cycle within snail

cercaria penetrates skin of man and enter blood vessels

snails

cercaria swims to infect man via hands, feet and mouth

fork-tailed cercaria floating upside-down in water

daughter sporocyst producing fork-tailed cercaria larvae

up in the tree-tops, sometimes coming out to bask on a branch. It is known to range from Burma to the Philippines but it may possibly live farther to the north, in Assam, Nepal and southern China. Little is known of its biology except that it eats mainly fruit and green shoots, its teeth being blunter than those of typical carnivores, but it also hunts small mammals and birds. FAMILY: Viverridaė, ORDER: Carnivora, CLASS: Mammalia.

BIOGEOCHEMICAL CYCLE, the natural process by which the chemical components of an animal's body, which are ultimately derived from its non-living environment, are returned to the environmental pool for re-use. Since the resources of the non-living environment are strictly limited, the existence of this mechanism is imperative to ensure that the building materials of future generations are not in short supply.

The word 'biogeochemical' informs us that we are dealing here with three major disciplines, biology, geology and chemistry. During its history a particular atom may at one time be a component of a rock, at another time be in a freely dissolved state and at another be incorporated in the body of a living organism. Such an atom may be said to have passed through an 'abiotic' (non-living, geological and chemical) phase and through a 'biotic' (when incorporated into a living organism) phase, and it may alternate between the two many times.

Such a system requires energy to drive it. This energy is ultimately derived from radiant solar energy, which is tapped by the process of photosynthesis carried out by green plants. In the course of this process a molecule of chlorophyll is 'excited' as a result of absorbing light energy. In returning to its normal state the chlorophyll molecule passes on the energy for storage in a chemical form, as adenosine triphosphate (ATP), which can then be used for carrying out work. This is the energy which drives the biogeochemical cycles.

One of the most important elements involved in the construction of living organisms is carbon, and the second part of the photosynthetic process is concerned with the fixation of carbon dioxide, that is the incorporation of carbon from carbon dioxide into complex organic compounds. This is the stage at which the carbon atom passes from its abiotic to its biotic phase. Carbon dioxide is reduced biochemically with an associated expenditure of energy to form first three carbon molecules and then more complex, energy-rich components of the plant's structure, e.g. sugars and starch. One of a number of possible fates may befall these high energy compounds: 1 They may be respired to give carbon dioxide and water so that their energy is released; 2 they may be eaten by a consumer animal (herbivore) or 3 they may

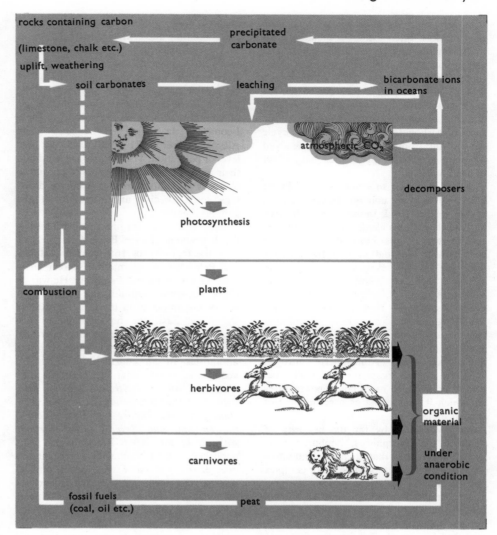

Diagram illustrating the carbon cycles: from the air through the photosynthesis of plants to processes on land and in the oceans.

be used as an energy source by decomposer organisms after the death of the plant. If eaten by a herbivore, the compounds may be reassembled within the animal body and then may again suffer one of the three possible fates, except that this time the consumer animal would be a predator.

Since both carbon fixation and respiration are oxidation/reduction reactions, the cycling of carbon is intimately linked with that of oxygen.

We have so far considered only the biotic phase in the cycling of carbon. Carbon enters its abiotic phase either in the form of dead organic compounds or as free carbon dioxide gas. As has been mentioned, the usual fate of complex organic compounds in nature is that they are respired by decomposers. Under certain conditions, however, this decay process may be impeded, e.g. in the environment of bogs and fens where there is little oxygen. Here organic debris may accumulate faster than it can be utilized by the decomposers, resulting in the formation of peat. Such deposits may in the

course of time develop into what we regard as fossil fuels such as coal and oil. In burning these materials we release both their stored energy and their carbon (as CO_2). Some scientists feel that this interruption of the natural cycling and storage system could have harmful effects, for to raise the atmospheric CO_2 level would increase the insulating properties of the earth's atmosphere and thereby raise earth temperatures. Theoretically the burning of fuels in the next 100 years could raise the CO_2 content of the atmosphere by between four and ten times. This would raise earth temperatures by 44°–53°F (7–12°C), a rise more than sufficient to melt the ice caps.

There is, however, another important consideration in the cycling of carbon, which is the solubility of CO_2 in the slightly alkaline waters of the oceans. Here CO_2 dissolves to form bicarbonate ions, $OH^- + CO_2 \rightleftharpoons HCO_3^-$.

This equilibrium maintains atmospheric CO_2 concentration at a very constant level of 0·03%. Carbon in this form may be removed from solution by combination with calcium, this process often being associated with living organisms, e.g. shellfish, corals and calcareous algae. Such deposits may eventually form calcareous rocks containing a store of carbon which is not released into the cycle again until the sediments are uplifted and the rocks weathered. Carbon, in the form of carbonates, then re-enters the cycle via the soil, from which it may be removed by plant growth or by the leaching effect of precipitation.

All of the 30 or so elements found in the bodies of animals undergo biogeochemical cycling of this kind, though the cyclic patterns of the various elements differ considerably in their details. For instance, nitrogen is somewhat unusual in that the gaseous reservoir of this element is only made available to higher plants and animals via a process of microbiological fixation. The agencies involved in this fixation include free-living soil microbes, symbiotic bacteria living in association with certain plants (e.g. legumes) and members of the blue green algae. Atmospheric nitrogen fixed by these organisms ultimately becomes available to more complex creatures for which it is essential as a component of protein molecules.

The cycling of by far the majority of elements, e.g. phosphorus, sulphur, etc., is rather simpler than that of carbon and nitrogen, involving no gaseous phase nor complex fixation process.

The importance of the delicate balance involved in these cycles has only recently become apparent to mankind. Where a soil is exploited for cereals, for forestry, for stock raising or for dairying, there is a continuous drain upon the resources of the system. Mineral elements, all of which are derived ultimately from the soil, are being removed in a variety of forms, as cereal grain, timber, meat and milk. Within the soil there occurs a replenishment process, namely the weathering of the parent rock, but if this does not occur fast enough to contend with the rate of harvesting, then fertility and yield will be reduced. In order to maintain an efficient system man must make up the soil deficit in added nutrients, i.e. he must add fertilizer. All conservation, then, must be based upon the understanding and maintenance of the biogeochemical cycles.   P.D.M.

BIOLOGICAL ART. Aristotle's works mark a break from superstition to accurate observation. The works of Pliny represent a retrogression. The medieval Bestiaries, the only natural history books of the Dark Ages, in Europe, were based on Pliny.

The pursuit of truth in biology, as opposed to superstition and legend, took a turn for the better with the Renaissance but only slight progress was made until the 16th

century, when zoology began to be a factual, discriminating and critical study.

The credit for these advances must go as much to the artists as to the savants. If Renaissance biology was superior to that of the Middle Ages, it is so for two reasons: the cultivation of precise description and the use of animal drawings. In the second of these Leonardo da Vinci (1452–1519) and Albrecht Durer (1471–1528) reached a high level of perfection. The tendency is to admire their animal drawings as works of art and to overlook the importance of accurate drawings in a precise understanding of the animals themselves.

Less well known for his contributions was the Frenchman Pierre Belon (1517–1564). Like the majority of 16th century naturalists, Belon was a polymath, a scholar interested in a wide range of subjects. He was as interested in the pyramids and the embalming of mummies as in the large animals of the Near East, the hippopotamuses and crocodiles. Above all, he became interested in the fishes, so often portrayed on Egyptian antiquities. In due course he published his account of them under the sonorous title: *Natural History of Strange Marine Fish, with their Portraits Engraved in Wood; including a True Picture and Description of the Dolphin and Several Other Strange Animals of this Kind*. Later, in 1555, he published another book, with a more modest title, *History of the Fishes*, which was to become the cornerstone of the science of ichthyology. This second work was incorporated by Konrad Gesner (1730–1788), the Swiss zoologist, in his *Historia Animalium* which for a century or more was Europe's most comprehensive source of information on animals.

A similar contribution was made by Bernard Palissy (1510–1589), a fellow countryman of Belon. Palissy was a potter, a man of little education and not primarily with a thirst for knowledge as such. He was interested in pottery with painted designs on it and among other things designed oval dishes known as *rustiques figurines* that were fashionable for long after Palissy had died miserably in the Bastille, denounced for having turned Protestant. Nevertheless, although single-minded about his pottery work he became interested in the origin of everything connected with his work. As a result he became something of a chemist, physicist, geologist and zoologist. His enamelled ware was decorated with drawings of shells, fishes, lizards and snakes.

This had a tremendous impact. In Palissy's days anyone interested in natural history was likely as not to take an interest in birds, to the exclusion of everything else, rather as today. Palissy, like Belon, helped to turn their eyes earthwards, even to look down into the waters, whether of rivers or

seas. He was commissioned by Catherine de Medici to make an animal grotto in the garden of the Tuileries. For this he left his native Perigord for Paris.

Palissy had collected fossils as well, purely at first for inspiration for his pottery designs. As a result, when he began giving public lectures in Paris, he could not only describe his animals but illustrate them with the pictures on his pottery and compare them with extinct animals demonstrated with his fossils.

Students flocked to his lectures, so did court society, which did nothing to make Palissy popular with the university and may have contributed to his incarceration in the Bastille. Ironically, we can see in Palissy's methods the prototype of a modern educational method involving the maximum use of visual aids. If this is true, then the action of the Parisian academics may have prevented the development of this aspect of education for a matter of 400 years.

The art of da Vinci, Dürer and Belon was on paper and therefore capable of reproduction in the printed form. The logical extension of this was the use of wood engravings, steel engravings and then lithography, giving finer and finer lines and details to the drawings as techniques improved. Colour pictures were, however, costly to produce so it followed inevitably that scientific journals and text-books were illustrated with black-and-white line-drawings almost entirely. A curious side-effect of this is that textbooks tend by tradition to be drab, and unexciting in their illustrations. Moreover, any book that is not drab is hard to accept as a textbook. The tradition is being broken down, but slowly, yet in biology especially colour is almost inseparable from a complete understanding of the living world.

Exceptions occur, as always, and the world of zoology must always be indebted to artists such as *Audubon and John Gould, and many more of almost equal merit if less known to such wide audiences, for the paintings, as accurate as they are beautiful, that they have bequeathed to us. Moreover, in the latter years of the 19th and the early years of this century a number of scientific books were beautifully illustrated in colour. The long series of reports of the 'Challenger' Expedition and the volumes published by the Prince of Monaco spring readily to mind. This era came to an end with the First World War and the international austerity which followed, but the use of colour in publishing has seen a revival within recent years owing to advances in printing techniques. The first fruits are seen mainly in so-called popular works, but the day may yet come when textbooks of biology will be as pleasant to the eye as these are without losing any of their value as purveyors of information. Indeed, they can hardly help to gain immensely from it.   M.B.